500 RECIPES
FOR SLIMMERS

500 RECIPES
FOR SLIMMERS

by Marguerite Patten

HAMLYN
LONDON · NEW YORK · SYDNEY · TORONTO

Contents

Cover photograph by Paul Williams

Published by The Hamlyn Publishing Group Limited
London · New York · Sydney · Toronto
Astronaut House, Feltham, Middlesex, England

© Copyright The Hamlyn Publishing Group Limited 1962

Twenty-third impression 1984

ISBN 0 600 03403 8

Printed and bound in Great Britain by R. J. Acford

his book does not set out any formal diets
all. If you are having to slim very drastic-
ly, for medical reasons, you will doubtless
ave been given a proper diet by your doctor.

owever, if you are trying to lose weight
radually or to retain your present weight
ithout any increase, you will find here about
)0 recipes that are meant for sensible eating.

here is such a diversity of diets today that
he best advice one can give is to find the diet
est suited to you, and stick to it.

Ve have all heard of the extreme diets:

he one in which you eat nothing but hard-
oiled eggs with a little sherry or port.
he banana and milk diet.
he bread and butter diet.
he diet in which one eats anything except
tarches and sugar.
he very drastic diets which are near starva-
ion and which produce, quite often, a most
mpressive drop in weight.

f your doctor has prescribed any one of these,
you can rest assured that it is all right for
you, but on the whole the medical profession
does not approve of these sudden, rather
cranky diets. The reasons are twofold. Everyone needs a reasonably well-balanced diet to
maintain good health and vitality. If you
suddenly stop eating most of the necessary
everyday foods, your health can suffer. It has
also been proved that when people lose an
enormous amount of weight very rapidly on
a drastic near-starvation diet, they tend to
put it back again the moment they start to
eat normal foods.

The ideal diet is one that keeps you fit and
with a feeling of well being, but not over-fed,
and which does, gradually, educate you to like
the foods that are good for you and avoid
those which put on weight rapidly. It is sur-
prising how much your eating habits can
change. People who have given up sweets for
quite a long time rarely find they want to eat
very many of them when their diet is ended.

What are the foods that are good for one?

Proteins: These are found in meat, fish, eggs,
cheese and to a lesser extent in
beans, peas, lentils and nuts. The
diet that is deficient in protein very
speedily results in your feeling
tired and listless.

Fats: To be found in butter, cheese,
cream, margarine, oil, cooking fat
etc. If you cut out fats completely
you lose a lot of your resistance to
colds and your skin suffers.

Carbo-hydrates: These are the sugars and
starches. The starches are to be
found in flour, and in some cornflour, cereals, vegetables like potatoes. The sugars in sweets, honey,
jams and of course sugar itself. If
you cut these out completely, you
are inclined to feel tired more
readily and also to feel cold.

Fresh fruits and vegetables: The vitamins
contained in these assist in keeping
one well and healthy.

The general opinion today is that you must
cut down a certain amount on all foods but
particularly on carbo-hydrates. Some diets
tell you to eat as much lean meat, fruit and
vegetables as you wish but to cut down
drastically on fats and carbo-hydrates. Other
diets set a calorie count, which means that
you can eat what you like, providing the total
sum of the food does not exceed the calories
necessary for you to lose weight.

If you are following this type of diet do follow
it intelligently. As you will see, 2 oz. of ice
cream has very much the same number of
calories as 2 oz. of lean mutton, but if you
want to keep well it is much more important
to eat meat than ice cream. If you are following a calorie diet, do pick out your protein
foods and allocate most of your daily calories
to that.

Many people have been disappointed on a diet
to find they don't lose weight the first week.
We all vary quite a lot. Some people lose
a great deal of weight to begin with and
then lose it at a much slower rate. Other
people, on the other hand, have to diet for
several weeks before any appreciable loss is
shown. If, however, your particular diet has
been followed VERY STRICTLY without
loss of weight, it indicates that, unfortunately
for you, it is a little too generous, and you
must cut down on the food you are eating.

One last word about all diets – DON'T
CHEAT. An odd biscuit here and there, or
even extra fruit if you've been rationed on
fruit, can undo all the good of several days'
careful eating.

Some Useful Facts and Figures

Comparison of Weights and Measures

English weights and measures have been used throughout the book. 3 teaspoonfuls equal 1 tablespoon. The average English teacup is $\frac{1}{4}$ pint. The average English breakfast cup is $\frac{1}{2}$ pint. When cups are mentioned in recipes they refer to a B.S.I. measuring cup which holds $\frac{1}{2}$ pint or 10 fluid ounces. In case it is wished to translate quantities into American of metric counterparts the following give a comparison.

Liquid measure

The American pint is 16 fluid ounces, as opposed to the British Imperial pint and Canadian pint which are 20 fluid ounces. The American $\frac{1}{2}$-pint measuring cup is therefore equivalent to $\frac{2}{3}$ British pint. In Australia the British Imperial pint, 20 fluid ounces, is used.

Solid measure

British	American
1 lb. butter or other fat	2 cups
1 lb. flour	4 cups
1 lb. granulated or castor sugar	2 cups
1 lb. sifted icing or confectioners' sugar	$3\frac{1}{2}$ cups
1 lb. brown (moist) sugar (firmly packed)	2 cups
12 oz. golden syrup or treacle	1 cup
14 oz. rice	2 cups
1 lb. dried fruit	3 cups
1 lb. chopped or minced meat (firmly packed)	2 cups
1 lb. lentils or split peas	2 cups
2 oz. soft breadcrumbs	1 cup
$\frac{1}{2}$ oz. flour	2 tablespoons
1 oz. flour	$\frac{1}{4}$ cup
1 oz. sugar	2 tablespoons
$\frac{1}{2}$ oz. butter	1 tablespoon
1 oz. golden syrup or treacle	1 tablespoon
1 oz. jam or jelly	1 tablespoon
All U.S. standard measuring cups and tablespoons	

To help you understand metrication

You will see from the chart that 1 oz. is approximately 28 g. but can be rounded off to the more convenient measuring unit of 25. Also the figures in the right hand column are not always increased by 25. This is to reduce the difference between the convenient number and the nearest equivalent.

The conversion chart

Ounces/fluid ounces	Approx. g. and ml. to nearest whole number	Recommended nearest unit of 25
1	28	25
2	57	50
3	85	75
4	113	125
5 ($\frac{1}{4}$ pint)	142	150
6	170	175
7	198	200
8 ($\frac{1}{2}$ lb.)	226	225
9	255	250
10 ($\frac{1}{2}$ pint)	283	275
12 ($\frac{3}{4}$ lb.)	340	350
15 ($\frac{3}{4}$ pint)	428	425
16 (1 lb.)	456	450
20 (1 pint)	569	575

Note: When converting quantities over 20 oz. first add the appropriate figures in the centre column, not those given in the right hand column, THEN adjust to the nearest unit of 25. It may be useful to note that 1 litre (1000 millilitres, 10 decilitres) equals 1·76 pints, or almost exactly $1\frac{3}{4}$ pints; 1 kilogramme (1000 grammes) equals 2·2 pounds, or almost exactly 2 lb. 3 oz.

Oven temperatures

The chart below gives conversions from degrees Fahrenheit to degrees Celsius recommended by manufacturers of electric cookers.

Description	°F.	°C.	Gas Mark
very cool	225	110	$\frac{1}{4}$
	250	120	$\frac{1}{2}$
cool	275	140	1
	300	150	2
moderate	325	160	3
	350	180	4
moderately hot	375	190	5
	400	200	6
hot	425	220	7
	450	230	8
very hot	475	240	9

Quantities in recipes

All recipes serve 4 unless otherwise stated.

Basic Methods of Cooking

Baking—Cooking in dry heat in the oven.

Boiling—Cooking by immersing the food in a pan of liquid, which must be kept boiling gently, all the time.

Braising—Almost a combination of stewing and roasting. Meat is placed on a bed of vegetables with a little liquid surrounding, in a covered vessel, and cooked slowly in the oven.

Casserole—Cooking slowly in the oven in a covered casserole dish—usually meat, rabbit etc.

Frying—Cooking in a little hot fat in an open pan. Deep frying is cooking by immersion in a deep pan of smoking hot fat.

Grilling—Cooking quickly under a red-hot grill; used for small tender pieces of meat, fish etc.

Poaching—Cooking gently in water which is just below boiling point; usually eggs or fish.

Pressure Cooking—Cooking at higher temperatures than usual, so that food is cooked much more quickly.

Roasting—Cooking with a little fat in a hot oven. Fat is poured from the baking tin over the meat or poultry from time to time, using a long-handled spoon: this is known as basting.

Simmering—the rate of cooking used for stews—just below boiling point, so that the liquid bubbles gently at the side of the pan.

Steaming—Cooking either in a steamer over a pan of boiling water, or in a basin standing in (but not covered by) boiling water.

Stewing—Cooking slowly until the food is tender. It is done in just enough liquid to cover the food, as the liquid is served with it and should be rich. Stews may be cooked in covered saucepans or casseroles, on a hotplate or in the oven, but always at a low temperature.

Leaving salt out of a diet

Some diets tell you to serve as little salt as possible with your foods. This means you must cut out the use of salt at the table, and as much as possible in cooking. Obviously if, for health reasons, you have been told 'no salt at all' the salt should be kept out of cooking entirely. The following suggestions will, I hope, assist you in making the food more appetising.

6 suggestions for flavouring salt-free dishes

Many starch-reduced products are very low in salt content but, of course, you cannot have them if you have to cut out salt completely. Here are a few suggestions for flavouring a salt-free diet.

Use pastry without salt.

Get a chemist to make up for you a salt-free baking powder from cream of tartar and tartaric acid.

There are 2 products which act rather as saccharine does to sugar called NEOSELAROM and ANALOS. Both contain potassium. NEOSELAROM is strongly flavoured so you will have to experiment to find out how much to use for your own taste. A good pinch of Neoselarom put in the water for boiling, and not scattered about on the food, ensures evenness of taste. When flavouring for sauces or thickening, mix it well with the dry ingredients. It doesn't sprinkle so if it is used on the plate indiscriminately it can taste bitter, but you can work out what suits you best. ANALOS is used in exactly the same way as Neoselarom.

4 A good grocer can supply salt-free vinegar.

5 Yeast extract is often free of salt and very good for flavouring savoury dishes.

6 Also one can buy salt-free margarine, butter and lard for cooking and eating, and you should have no difficulty in finding shops which stock these products.

Hors-d'Oeuvre, Soups, Party Time

Hors-d'oeuvre for slimmers

When you are planning your own meals it is wise to leave out a first course and just have the main course plus fruit or cheese. However, if you are eating with the rest of the family, or with friends, you may feel you want to join in and have what they are eating.

You have two alternatives, firstly to plan an hors-d'oeuvre that everyone can eat and yet fits into most diets. The next few pages give you some ideas which are delicious.

The second alternative, of course, is to give the rest of the family one thing while you have a different dish.

The soup section includes a number of recipes for you to make for all the family, because, while they are less fattening than most soups, they give a feeling of well-being and don't blunt the appetite for the main dish.

If by chance you are choosing a fish course as an hors-d'oeuvre (smoked salmon, shell fish cocktail etc.), give yourself a smaller portion of fish than everyone else, and be rather more generous with the lettuce and other less fattening foods.

Tip to dieters

When eating an hors-d'oeuvre in a restaurant there are certain foods you are wise to avoid:

Rollmop herrings, sardines, baked beans, eggs or salad in a heavy mayonnaise.

Choose just the vegetable ingredients of an hors-d'oeuvre.

Avocado pear hors-d'oeuvre

This makes an excellent hors-d'oeuvre by itself or served with shrimps or prawns.

Halve the avocado pear and take out the centre stone. Serve with the low calorie French dressing (page 45).

Avocado pear and shrimps

Prepare the avocado pear as above, and fill the centre with prawns or shrimps and a small amount of slimming French dressing (page 45).

Fish cocktails

no cooking

Use fresh or canned shell fish of any kind.
1 Prepare the cooked fish, cutting it into sma pieces or flaking if necessary, when cooked.
2 Mix with seasoning, lemon juice or goo quality vinegar, or low calorie tomato sala dressing (page 45).
3 Line some small glasses with lettuce leave and put in the fish mixture.
4 Garnish each glass with chopped parsley lemon, a prawn or shrimp head or a tin lobster claw.

Grape and orange cocktail

no cooking

you will need:

4 oranges	8 oz. grapes

1 Remove the flesh from 3 of the oranges taking off any pith and skin.
2 Combine with some skinned, halved grape and well cover with orange juice from the fourth orange.
3 Put into individual glasses and chill thoroughly before serving.

Grapefruit cocktail

no cooking

you will need:

2 large grapefruit	orange
little lemon juice or sherry	sprigs of mint
few fresh grapes	very little sugar

1 Try to prepare this in the morning so that the fruit stands during the day.
2 Halve the grapefruit, remove the sections and mix with the stoned halved grapes and pieces of orange.
3 Pile back into the grapefruit cases, sprinkle with sugar and lemon juice or sherry.
4 Just before serving top with sprigs of mint.

Grapefruit and orange cocktail

no cooking

you will need:

2 grapefruit	cherries
2 oranges	

1 Cut oranges and grapefruit in half and remove the flesh.
2 Mix together and replace in the grapefruit skins with a cherry.

Melon and ginger cocktail

no cooking

you will need:

cubes of melon | ½ teaspoon powdered
tablespoon lemon juice | ginger

Mix ginger and lemon juice together and pour over melon.
Chill the mixture and serve in cocktail glasses.

Orange mint cocktail

no cooking

you will need:

sharp-flavoured oranges | chopped mint
tablespoons lemon juice

Skin the oranges, remove all pith and pips, divide into pieces and chill thoroughly.
Place the pieces of orange in small glasses with the lemon juice and sprinkle with freshly chopped mint.

Pineapple and melon cocktail

no cooking

you will need:

ripe melon | mint leaves
diced fresh pineapple | squeeze lemon juice
little sherry if wished | sugar*

*Or use little diluted sugar substitute.

Mix the pineapple and melon together in a bowl, cutting both into small easy to serve dice. Or, if you have a vegetable scoop, the melon can be cut into balls.
Mix with a little lemon juice, sherry and sugar and leave in a really cold place.
Pile into glasses and top with mint when ready to serve.

Pineapple and orange juice cocktail

no cooking

you will need:

pineapple juice | orange juice
water

Mix together 1 part pineapple juice, 3 parts orange juice and 2 parts water (or more if liked).
Chill thoroughly and serve in small glasses.
Remember that sweetened juice has a high percentage of sugar, so even if you use canned sweetened pineapple juice have *fresh* orange juice.

Southern melon

5 Servings

cooking time   20 minutes

you will need:

2 oz. quick cooking macaroni | 1 medium sized melon
1 dessertspoon castor sugar | 2 oz. cleaned sultanas
 | 1 small jar yoghourt

1 Cook macaroni. Drain.
2 Cut top off melon.
3 Scoop out inside of melon and chop roughly.
4 Drain juice from melon.
5 Mix yoghourt, sugar, melon, sultanas and macaroni thoroughly together.
6 Pile mixture into melon shell. Replace top. Chill. Serve.

Tomato juice cocktail

no cooking

you will need:

½ pint tomato juice | few drops Worcester-
2 tablespoons lemon juice | shire sauce
pinch celery salt | ½ teaspoon salt
cayenne pepper

1 Put the tomato juice in a jug and add the remaining ingredients.
2 Chill.

Vegetable cocktail

no cooking

you will need:

lightly cooked or raw diced small carrots, onion, green peas, French beans etc. | seasoning
 | lettuce hearts
 | chopped herbs
salad dressing (page 44)

1 Cut the vegetables into small dice, season and toss in salad dressing.
2 Serve in individual glasses with a few small leaves of lettuce and garnish with chopped fresh herbs.

Low calorie vegetable hors-d'oeuvre

A very colourful and, at the same time, slimming hors-d'oeuvre can be made as follows:
1 Rings of cucumber sprinkled with a little lemon juice or vinegar and red pepper.
2 Tomato slices tossed in French dressing (page 45) and chopped chives.
3 Sprigs of raw or cooked cauliflower topped with one of the slimming dressings and chopped parsley.

4 Raw mushrooms sliced thinly and tossed in low calorie French dressing (page 45).

5 Grated carrot mixed with a little chopped parsley and grated cheese.

6 Balls of cottage cheese dusted with red pepper and parsley on the outside.

Serving soups when dieting

In cold weather particularly, a good soup is a first class start to the meal and if you have been in the habit of serving soup, this is something you will miss a great deal. I have, therefore, included some soup recipes which, while they cannot all be described as very slimming, are certainly lower on calories than the average.

Clear beetroot soup

2 Servings

cooking time   1 hour 20 minutes

you will need:

1 small beetroot, cooked or uncooked	1 good teaspoon lemon juice
good pinch sugar	$\frac{3}{4}$ pint chicken or beef
seasoning	stock

1 If using an uncooked beetroot, cook steadily until soft, then cut into very tiny shreds. Keep a teaspoon of these for a garnish.

2 Put the rest of the beetroot into the saucepan with all other ingredients and cook for about 20 minutes.

3 Rub through a sieve or beat well until no pieces remain, then reheat.

4 Pour into soup cup and garnish with the strips of beetroot.

This can be served cold or hot.

Chicken purée soup

cooking time $1\frac{1}{2}$ hours

you will need:

5 oz. cooked chicken meat	1 dessertspoon cornflour
bones of a chicken	tiny knob of butter
seasoning	2 pints water
	$\frac{1}{2}$ pint milk

1 Simmer the carcass in the water for 1 hour, then strain.

2 Add the cooked chicken meat and milk and cook for a further 15 minutes, then rub through a sieve.

3 Blend with cornflour, add butter, seasoning.

4 Cook for 10 minutes.

Clear mushroom soup

cooking time   5–10 minute

you will need:

1 pint chicken stock, or water and 2 chicken bouillon cubes	6 oz. mushrooms seasoning parsley

1 Chop the mushrooms very finely indeed an simmer for 5–10 minutes in the stock.

2 Garnish with a little chopped parsley.

Clear onion soup

1 Serving

cooking time   20 minute

you will need:

$\frac{1}{4}$ oz. butter	1 starch-reduced roll
1 onion	$\frac{1}{2}$ oz. grated cheese
$\frac{1}{2}$ pint clear stock	pinch sage
yeast extract	

1 Grate the onion, toss in the butter, then add the stock (flavoured with yeast extract).

2 Season well, adding pinch sage and simmer for 20 minutes.

3 Pour into hot soup cup, cut the roll in half, drop into soup with cut side uppermost, sprinkle lightly with cheese and brown under grill.

Clear tomato soup

cooking time   25 minutes

Make tomato soup as directed on page 11. Reheat after putting through muslin. If a slightly thickened soup is desired, it will only be necessary to rub through the sieve without straining afterwards.

Consommé

cooking time   1 hour–1 hour 20 minutes

you will need:

12 oz. shin of beef	1 carrot
2 pints good stock	small piece celery
seasoning	sprig parsley
1 onion	bay leaf

1 Cut the meat into small pieces and put them into the saucepan together with the other ingredients.

2 Simmer very gently for 1 hour, then strain through several thicknesses of muslin.

3 Add a dessertspoon sherry if desired.

4 To clear a consommé, put in a stiffly beaten egg white and clean egg shell and gently simmer again for 20 minutes, then re-strain.

Cucumber soup

cooking time   20 minutes

you will need:

1 cucumber	3–4 tablespoons thick
1 oz. butter	cream*
1 pint white stock	salt and pepper
(or water)	½ pint milk
1 egg	
parsley	

*Omit if you are watching your intake of fat.

1 Peel cucumber and cut it in half lengthways.
2 Remove seeds and cut the remainder into small pieces.
3 Melt butter in a thick pan.
4 Gradually add stock. Bring to boil.
5 Add cucumber, salt and pepper to taste and simmer until cucumber is tender.
6 Pour soup through a sieve, beating cucumber to a thin purée.
7 Return to pan.
8 In a small pan bring the milk to boil and stir it into the soup.
9 Beat up egg, remove soup from heat, stir in egg and serve immediately, garnished with chopped chervil or parsley.
The cream should be added for the non-slimmers only with the egg.

Curried consommé

cooking time   10–15 minutes

you will need:

1 good-sized onion	1 teaspoon curry powder
1½ pints clear stock	seasoning
½ oz. butter	

1 Heat the butter, stir in the curry powder.
2 Add the stock and the very finely chopped onion and simmer for approximately 15 minutes.
3 Season well.

Egg soup

1–2 Servings

cooking time   13 minutes

you will need:

1 teaspoon yeast extract	1 egg
seasoning	1 pint water or stock
1 dessertspoon rice	

1 Dissolve the yeast extract in the hot water or stock, add the rice and cook steadily for 10 minutes.
2 Stir in any extra seasoning.
3 Beat the egg well, then stir into the hot, but not boiling, soup.
4 Cook gently without boiling for a further 3 minutes.

Fish soup

1 Serving

cooking time   15 minutes

you will need:

4 oz. white fish	1 teaspoon finely chopped
½ pint milk	chives (a little grated
seasoning	onion could be used
1 teaspoon flour	instead)
tiny knob of butter	pinch nutmeg
about ¼ pint water	

1 Cut the fish into tiny pieces and put in a saucepan.
2 Add the water and a little salt.
3 Cook for about 5 minutes.
4 Blend the flour with the milk and add this and the other ingredients.
5 Cook steadily for further 10 minutes.
This soup is substantial enough to form a good evening meal with starch-reduced roll.

Iced cucumber soup

cooking time   15 minutes

you will need:

1 medium sized cucumber	2 tablespoons milk
1 small chopped onion	seasoning
½ oz. butter	lemon
½ pint stock	

1 Cut cucumber into pieces, leaving on some of the peel.
2 Fry onion in butter, add cucumber, half the stock, seasoning and simmer gently for about 15 minutes.
3 Put through sieve or into electric blender.
4 Add milk and rest of stock, when cold pour into freezing tray, leave until lightly frosted.
5 Serve in soup cups garnished with lemon.

Iced tomato soup

cooking time   25 minutes

you will need:

1½ lb. tomatoes	1 small chopped onion
1 pint water or white stock	few drops Worcestershire
½ small beetroot,	sauce
preferably uncooked	1 teaspoon vinegar or
small pieces of celery	lemon juice
2 bay leaves	seasoning

1 Put the ingredients all together in a large saucepan and cook gently until the tomatoes are very soft. This should take about 25 minutes.
2 Remove the beetroot and bay leaves then rub through a sieve and finally strain through muslin.
3 Pour into freezing tray of refrigerator and leave for a short time, until slightly iced.
4 Serve garnished with lemon.

Jellied tomato consommé

cooking time   5–10 minutes

you will need:

about 1½ pint tomato juice (canned or bottled)	1 tablespoon finely chopped onion or chives
good pinch celery salt	seasoning
1 bouillon cube	1 level tablespoon powdered gelatine
¼ pint water or white stock	mint

To garnish:
small wedges of lemon

1 Dissolve the bouillon cube in the water or stock, add to the tomato juice and simmer with the onion for about 5–10 minutes.
2 Pour over the powdered gelatine, which can be softened in tablespoon cold water, stir until thoroughly dissolved.
3 Season well.
4 Allow to cool and just begin to stiffen, then whisk lightly with a fork and pile into very cold soup cups.
5 Garnish with sprigs of mint and serve with lemon.

Lemon soup

cooking time   few minutes

you will need:

1 pint chicken stock	1 egg
2 tablespoons lemon juice	seasoning

1 Heat the stock. Beat the lemon juice and egg.
2 Whisk into the stock together with seasoning and simmer without boiling for a few minutes.

Lettuce soup

cooking time   10 minutes

you will need:

½–1 onion	½ lettuce
2 tomatoes	seasoning
1 pint stock	

1 Grate half large onion (or 1 small onion) and the sliced, skinned tomatoes.
2 Simmer in the clear stock until tender.
3 Add finely shredded lettuce and seasoning.
4 Cook steadily for 10 minutes.

Madrilène soup

cooking time   1 hour

you will need:

1 pint chicken stock, or water with 2 chicken bouillon cubes	1 pint beef stock, or water with 1 beef bouillon cube
8 oz. carrots	8 oz. tomatoes
1 onion	2 leeks
	seasoning

1 Bring bouillons and vegetables to the boil and simmer for 1 hour, adding salt and pepper when partly cooked.
2 Strain, and serve as a clear soup.

Mock turtle soup

8–10 Servings

cooking time   2–3 hours

you will need:

small calf's head	sherry or Madeira
water	bouquet garni
seasoning	

1 Wash the calf's head, split down the centre, remove brains if wished to use for a separate dish (also the tongue can be taken out).
2 Cover with cold water, bring to the boil, throw away the water and cover with fresh water, add seasoning and herbs and simmer gently until tender, about 2–3 hours.
3 Strain off the stock and put into a pan.
4 Cut the meat from the head.
5 Clear the stock as described on page 10, add the diced meat and heat gently. Put in sherry or Madeira just before serving.

Mussel soup

cooking time   20 minutes

you will need:

2 pints mussels	2 tablespoons finely chopped celery
1 finely chopped onion	1½ pints water
1 large skinned chopped tomato	squeeze lemon juice or little vinegar
small bunch parsley	
seasoning	

1 Scrub mussels well, discarding any that are open and will not close when sharply tapped.
2 Put into a large saucepan with onion, celery, parsley and seasoning and heat slowly until mussels open.
3 Remove mussels from liquid, take off shells. Always remove the 'beard' (the rather stringy part) from the mussels.
4 Meanwhile reheat liquid and cook the chopped tomato and seasoning until tender.
5 Remove sprig of parsley, add mussels and lemon juice or vinegar and reheat gently.
6 Garnish with chopped parsley.

Queen soup

2 Servings

cooking time   10–15 minutes

you will need:

½ pint chicken stock	1 dessertspoon sherry
seasoning	2 tablespoons milk
egg yolk	

1 Put all ingredients together into double saucepan and cook gently until the soup thickens slightly.
2 Do not allow to boil.

Quick-to-make consommé

You can buy cans of consommé which just have to be heated, adding a little lemon juice or sherry if desired.

The very excellent bouillon cubes or meat and vegetable cubes and extracts now available also provide the basis of stock or clear soup which can then be varied in a number of ways.

Quick vegetable soup

cooking time   10 minutes

you will need:

approximately 1 lb. mixed vegetables*	1½ pints stock or water with bouillon cube
chopped parsley	grated cheese
seasoning	

*Do choose a good mixture of vegetables for an interesting flavour. Use no potatoes and not too many carrots in this.

1 Peel and grate the vegetables on a coarse grater.
2 Bring the stock or water and bouillon cube to the boil, add the vegetables and seasoning and cook rapidly for about 5–8 minutes until the vegetables are just tender.
3 Pour into hot soup cups and sprinkle with lots of grated cheese and parsley.

Tomato and celery soup

cooking time   15–20 minutes

you will need:

1 lb. tomatoes	2 oz. butter
small head celery	1½ pints water or white stock
salt and pepper	
pinch brown sugar	½ oz. cornflour

1 Chop the tomatoes and celery into small pieces and simmer with 1 pint of the stock and seasoning until soft.
2 Rub through a sieve, then return to saucepan, together with the butter and the cornflour, blended with the other ½ pint water or stock.
3 Bring to the boil and cook until thickened, adding the sugar and extra seasoning if required.

Vegetable soup

2 Servings

cooking time   15–20 minutes

you will need:

8 oz. diced vegetables (carrot, tomato, turnip, onion, leek and/or celery, but NOT potatoes or parsnips)	1 pint VERY CLEAR meat stock with all fat removed, or vegetable stock
seasoning	parsley

1 Prepare and dice vegetables.
2 Simmer in stock for about 15 minutes.
3 Season well and garnish with chopped parsley. This non-thickened soup has an excellent flavour and helps to avoid the feeling of 'being hungry'.

What to eat at parties

A cocktail party, whether you give it yourself or are invited to one, is a 'snare and a delusion' if you are trying to lose weight. Beware of all those tiny, delicious titbits on crisp toast, biscuits or fried bread.

Obviously if you are attending somebody else's party you will just have to look round and either decline anything to eat, which makes everyone feel a little uncomfortable, or select your food carefully.

If you are planning your own cocktail party, life is much more simple because you can make certain you have low calorie foods to eat.

The following pages will suggest some of them but here is a good selection:

Cocktail savouries

Cubes of cheese on sticks in melon.
Prawns.
Cottage cheese balls.
Quarters of curried egg: Hard-boil the eggs, halve carefully, take out the yolk. Mash with a little low calorie salad dressing (page 45) and curry powder and replace in the white cases.
Diced melon or fresh pineapple on cocktail sticks.
Diced melon with lean ham on cocktail sticks.
Chicory or celery curls or stuffed celery (page 14).
Strips of crisp raw carrot.

Tips to dieters

At parties, remember to AVOID potato crisps and salted nuts. But you CAN eat gherkins and olives.

Stuffed prunes

no cooking

Stone some large, juicy prunes, which should be lightly cooked, and fill with any of the following mixtures:

1 Chopped cooked bacon or ham with piquant sauce.
2 Chopped gherkins and mayonnaise (page 45).
3 Chopped apple and watercress.
4 Cottage cheese.

Stuffed celery sticks

no cooking

Cut sticks of celery into even-sized lengths and fill the centre of each with one of the following mixtures:

1 Cream or cottage cheese and chopped nuts.
2 Diced apple and cream or cottage cheese.
3 Sieved hard-boiled egg and chutney.
4 Flaked crabmeat and salad dressing (page 45).
5 Very few chopped dates and apple.
6 Cottage cheese topped with paprika pepper.

Sweet dip

no cooking

you will need:

1 lb. cottage cheese	1 tablespoon honey
few blanched almonds	1 gill strawberry-flavoured
1 tablespoon lemon juice	yoghourt

1 Cut almonds into thin slices and toast in oven or under grill.
2 Sieve cottage cheese and blend with yoghourt, honey and lemon juice.
3 Place in a bowl and sprinkle toasted, slivered almonds over the top.

Melon balls

no cooking

you will need:

1 large melon	sprigs of mint

1 Cut melon into balls and put on to toothpicks.
2 Pile into melon halves and garnish with mint.
3 Chill thoroughly before serving.

This delectable low-calorie appetizer is ideal for a party and can be eaten with a free conscience.

What to drink at parties

Many people are very clever at making one drink last a very long time. If this is the case then you can choose your favourite drink. Otherwise it will be safer to select tomato juice, tonic or some other non-alcoholic drink.

Stuffed cucumber lengths

no cooking

you will need:

1 large cucumber, straight-sided, fresh, crisp	4 oz. poached salmon fresh, (or canned may be used)
lemon juice	
1 or 2 finely chopped stuffed olives	1 or 2 stuffed olives for garnish

1 Peel cucumber across in 1–1¼ inch lengths. Scoop out centres to form hollows.
2 Flake salmon, carefully removing bones and skin.
3 Mix with a little mayonnaise, sprinkle with lemon juice and finely chopped stuffed olives.
4 Pile into hollowed-out cucumber lengths and garnish with slices of stuffed olives, cut so that every slice has a red centre.

These stuffed cucumbers make excellent hors-d'oeuvre, or they can be served with drinks instead of the more conventional canapés.

Savoury eggs

cooking time   10 minutes

you will need:

½ hard-boiled egg each person	anchovies or anchovy paste
salt and pepper	toast fingers
grated cheese	

1 Hard-boil the eggs.
2 Cut through the middle and put the yolks through a sieve.
3 Mix yolks with salt, pepper and grated cheese.
4 Fill whites with mixture and dust with grated cheese.
5 Brown under the grill.
6 Spread toast fingers with pounded anchovies or anchovy paste.
7 Arrange eggs on toast fingers and serve very hot.

To fry or not to fry while dieting

On many slimming diets it is 'taboo' to fry any food at all. Other well known diet experts consider that fat can be included in the diet and have no objection to frying. If this is the case then you can certainly do so.

Very often recipes for frying state the food should be cooked in batter, flour or egg and crumbs. Quite obviously this will add more starch and, in consequence, more weight. There is little way round making a batter. You can of course have only a very thin coating, and use water instead of milk but, even so, you must use flour.

The best method is egg and crumbs. I have found that the starch-reduced bread, rolls or crispbread can be crumbled finely and used for coating. You then have a crisp attractive appearance on fish etc. but a lower calorie value.

Use really good pans for they mean you need less fat than if you have a thin, rather poor quality one. If you brush the pan well with oil you are using less fat. This method cannot of course, be used in every case but is certainly very good with rather fat fish or meat.

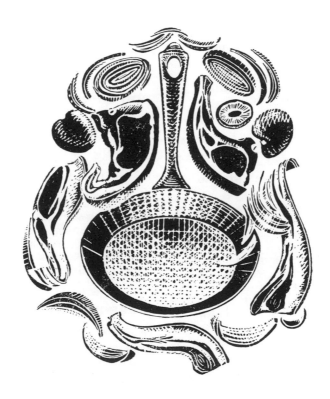

Fish

Cooking fish for slimmers

Fish is an excellent source of protein. At the same time, if you look at your calorie chart on page 83, you will find it is not unduly high in these. It is also sustaining and therefore a very good choice for a slimming diet.

Unfortunately many people consider fish is only at its best when fried. You will find suggestions on page 15 for cutting down the fattening properties of coating and below suggestions for oven frying.

However, if you intend to fry fish for your family, there is no reason why you can't have it, but take care to discard most of the fattening coating.

Shellfish is a very good buy for you, for whether you choose prawns, shrimps, lobster or crab, you will find that it is a slimming dish because it is very pleasant without a lot of extra sauces etc., added.

Make a good friend of your grill for grilled fish is easy to digest, easy to cook and very excellent to eat.

Serve plenty of attractive looking salads with the fish to give it colour and interest.

Oven frying of fish

1 Coat the fish as recommended on page 15.
2 Brush the baking tin with a very small amount of fat and put it in the oven to get really hot.
3 Lift the tin out carefully, put on the fish and just brush very lightly with a little more melted butter.
4 Cook for about 15 minutes if thin pieces of fish, 20–25 minutes if thick pieces, in a moderately hot oven (400°F.—Gas Mark 5).

To bake fish in foil

You will keep the flavour of the fish and avoid using much fat if you bake it wrapped up either in foil or greaseproof bags.
1 Season the fish, add the squeeze of lemon juice and wrap carefully in greased foil or a bag.
2 Bake thin fillets of fish for approximately 20 minutes and thicker pieces from 25–30 minutes in a moderately hot oven (400°F.— Gas Mark 5).
3 Unwrap just before serving and there is the fish complete with juice, so keeping it moist, and avoiding the necessity of any sauce.

To cook fish without fat

cooking time   10 minutes
1 Clean fish thoroughly, then put on a piece of greaseproof paper or foil, sprinkling over a little salt, pepper and lemon juice.
2 Wrap up the fish thoroughly, this makes certain that all the flavour is retained.
3 Put between two plates and stand over a saucepan of boiling water.
4 Cook for approximately 10 minutes until just tender.

Brochettes of bacon and escallops

cooking time   5–8 minutes
1 Cut escallops in halves, or in quarters, if very large.
2 Cut rashers of bacon into pieces long enough to roll round each piece of fish (3–4 inches long).
3 Wrap the escallops in bacon and put 3 or 4 of these on to skewers.
4 Cook under the grill, turning several times until bacon is crisp and escallops tender.
5 Serve on skewers with crisp salad. Garnish with lemon or sliced pineapple.

Casserole of cod and cider

cooking time   25 minutes

you will need:

2 wafer-thin, sliced onions	4 cutlets of cod
3 large thickly sliced tomatoes	½ pint cider seasoning
lemon, parsley to garnish	

1 Put the neat cutlets of cod into a dish, cover with thinly sliced onion, tomato, seasoning.
2 Add cider.
3 Bake for 25 minutes in a moderately hot oven (400°F.—Gas Mark 5).

Chaudfroid of haddock

cooking time   10–15 minutes

you will need:

1 lb. fish—large fillet of fresh haddock gherkin, tomato and radish to garnish	2 tablespoons milk $\frac{1}{4}$ pint aspic jelly

1 Cook the fish by steaming or boiling, being careful not to break it.
2 Make the aspic jelly, following instructions on jar or packet, but using some of the fish stock.
3 When this is cold and just beginning to set, fold it into the milk.
4 Carefully mask the cold fillet of haddock.
5 Garnish.
6 Serve on a bed of salad.

Cod with bacon

cooking time   25 minutes baking
                    10 minutes if grilling

you will need:

approximately 6 rashers bacon	1 lb. cod parsley to garnish

1 Cut the cod in thin strips, roll a rasher of bacon round each.
2 Bake in a moderate oven (375°F.—Gas Mark 4) or grill.

Cod's roe

cooking time   10 minutes

1 Steam the roe for about 10 minutes, then remove the outer skin.
2 Cut into slices which are delicious fried with bacon or served with salad.

Crab au gratin

1 Dress the crab (page 22) and return to the shell.
2 Sprinkle the top with a little cheese and brown under a moderately hot grill.

Creamed shrimps

cooking time   10 minutes

you will need:

8 oz. shrimps	lettuce
1 oz. margarine	seasoning
3 tablespoons milk	lemon
4 tomatoes	parsley

1 Halve the tomatoes and cook steadily under the grill.
2 Meanwhile heat the margarine, milk and seasoning.

3 Put in the shrimps and cook for just a few minutes.
4 Top each cooked half tomato with shrimps and garnish with lemon, parsley and lettuce.

Curried haddock and salad

no cooking

you will need:

1 lb. cooked, fresh haddock	2 tablespoons salad dressing (page 44)
1 dessertspoon curry powder	1 small sweet apple
lettuce	gherkins or cucumber
tomatoes	lettuce or watercress
3 spring onions	

1 Peel the apple and chop or grate finely.
2 Mix the curry in with the apple and chopped onion.
3 Put the onion, curry and apple into the salad dressing and mix thoroughly.
4 Flake the fish, but not too finely.
5 Arrange this on lettuce leaves and pour over the curried salad dressing.
6 Garnish with lettuce or watercress, sliced tomatoes and cucumber or gherkin.

Devilled fish

cooking time dependent on method of cooking

Any fish will have a more piquant flavour if you add a little curry powder and a few drops of Worcestershire sauce to the melted butter. Brush the fish with this and then grill or bake.

Devilled herrings

2 Servings

cooking time   25 minutes

you will need:

2 good-sized herrings	$\frac{1}{2}$ oz. grated onion
$\frac{1}{2}$ teaspoon Worcestershire sauce	1 teaspoon vinegar
$\frac{1}{2}$ teaspoon mustard	1 teaspoon sugar
$\frac{1}{2}$ oz. margarine	pinch salt

1 Split the herrings and take out the backbones.
2 Cream the margarine, add the mustard, onion, sugar, vinegar, Worcestershire sauce and salt.
3 Spread this paste on to the herrings. Roll tightly.
4 Put the fish wrapped in greaseproof paper in dish.
5 Cook for 25 minutes in a moderately hot oven.

Devilled crab

2 Servings

cooking time   4–10 minutes

you will need:

1 medium crab	1 teaspoon mixed
1 tablespoon starch-	mustard
reduced breadcrumbs	½ teaspoon Worcester-
seasoning	shire sauce
	1 teaspoon oiled butter

1 Mix crab meat with all seasonings etc.
2 Put back into shell, cover with breadcrumbs and the butter and brown under the grill or in the oven.

Fish in savoury custard

cooking time   1 hour

you will need:

12 oz. white fish	little butter
½ pint milk	2 eggs (or egg yolks)
seasoning	pinch thyme
lemon and parsley to	little chopped parsley
garnish	and/or grated onion

1 Butter a dish and put in the fish, season.
2 Beat eggs well, add milk, seasoning and flavourings.
3 Pour over fish and bake in a slow oven (275–300°F.—Gas Mark 2) for about 1 hour.
4 Garnish with lemon and parsley.

Fish mousse

cooking time   10–12 minutes
                          to thicken egg yolks

you will need:

2 teaspoons powdered	½ pint water
gelatine	2 teaspoons sherry (not
8 oz. cooked flaked fish	essential)
2 eggs	shredded lettuce leaves
2 teaspoons lemon juice	
seasoning	

1 Separate the egg yolks from the white and beat the yolks together with lemon juice and seasoning over a pan of hot water until slightly thickened.
2 Continue beating until cooler, then add the gelatine, dissolved in the very hot water, the sherry and fish.
3 When quite cold and just beginning to stiffen fold in the stiffly-beaten egg whites.
4 Put into glass dish and serve with shredded lettuce leaves.

Fillets of plaice délice

cooking time   10 minutes

you will need:

8 small fillets plaice	4 oz. black grapes
seasoning	tomato, cucumber or
salad dressing (page 44)	other salad ingredients
lettuce leaves	

1 Skin the fillets, season and fold in half.
2 Steam between two plates, then set aside to cool.
3 When cold, coat with salad dressing, allow to drain, then arrange on a bed of lettuce with the narrow ends of the fillets towards the centre.
4 Arrange several halved grapes, cut side down, on each fillet and garnish with other salad ingredients.

Fish custard

cooking time   50 minutes

you will need:

1 lb. uncooked white fish	1 large egg or yolks of
½ pint milk	2 eggs
½ teaspoon finely chopped	toast
parsley	lemon
seasoning	

1 Cut the fish into neat pieces.
2 Put at the bottom of a pie dish.
3 Beat the egg and pour over the hot but NOT boiling milk.
4 Add seasoning and parsley, then pour over the fish.
5 Stand the dish in another containing cold water and bake for approximately 45 minutes in the centre of a very moderate oven (350°F. —Gas Mark 3).
6 Garnish with lemon and triangles of toast.

Fish pudding

6–8 Servings

cooking time   30–45 minutes

you will need:

1½–2 lb. hake or cod	½ oz. cornflour
2 eggs	2 tablespoons milk, or
seasoning	cream from the top of
2 oz. margarine or butter	milk

1 Bone the uncooked fish and put it through a mincer twice so that it is very fine and smooth.
2 Melt the margarine, then add this to the fish, together with the other ingredients. The eggs should be well beaten and added 1 at a time.
3 Put the mixture into a well greased basin and cover with margarined paper and a cloth.
4 Either steam for 45 minutes, or stand the pudding in a dish of cold water in a moderate oven (375°F.—Gas Mark 4) and cook for 30 minutes.
5 To make an even lighter pudding, separate the egg yolks from the whites, add the yolks first, then FOLD in the stiffly beaten egg whites.

Fish Florentine

2 Servings

cooking time   15 minutes

you will need:

4 fillets plaice
2 tablespoons white wine or lemon juice
1 small packet frozen spinach
2 oz. grated cheese
seasoning

1 Fold each fillet in 3, place in a greased baking dish.
2 Sprinkle with wine or lemon juice, and seasoning.
3 Cover with buttered paper and bake in a moderate oven for 10 minutes.
4 Meanwhile cook spinach, drain well. Add 1½ oz. cheese to this.
5 Place spinach in a heatproof dish, put fish on top.
6 Sprinkle with remaining cheese and brown under grill.

Fish rollmops

2 Servings

cooking time   20 minutes

you will need:

2 small fillets of plaice, or whiting
1 teaspoon chopped parsley
juice of ½ lemon
water
seasoning
bay leaf
pinch mixed spice
½ oz. margarine

1 Mix the parsley, margarine and a little lemon juice together.
2 Add seasoning.
3 Put this on to the fillets of fish and roll them tightly.
4 Put into a dish, adding just enough water to half cover, the remaining lemon juice, seasoning, spice and bay leaf.
5 Put a cover on the dish and cook steadily in the oven for 20 minutes (400°F.—Gas Mark 4–5).
6 Serve hot or cold.

Grilled escallops (or scallops)

cooking time   5–6 minutes

These delicious shell fish keep all their flavour when grilled.

1 Remove from the shell, wash and brush with little melted butter.
2 Cook steadily, turning well until tender.
3 Garnish with lemon, chopped parsley and red pepper.
4 If preferred roll escallops first in melted butter then in soft breadcrumbs (preferably starch-reduced crumbs) before grilling.

Grilled herrings

cooking time   10 minutes

1 Season the herrings well and brush with a very small amount of melted fat.
2 Cook steadily under a grill allowing about 5 minutes on either side.

Grilled sole or plaice with grapes

cooking time   8–10 minutes

you will need:

4 medium sized sole or plaice
seasoning
slices of lemon
8 oz. grapes
very little butter

1 Halve and pip the grapes and put in the grill pan.
2 Brush the grid of the grill pan with the hot butter, and the well seasoned fish with hot butter, and add a squeeze of lemon juice.
3 Cook steadily until tender on one side, turn and cook on the second side. It is advisable to cook the dark-skinned side first.
4 Garnish with the grapes and slices of lemon.

Hake Portuguese

cooking time   25–30 minutes

you will need:

4 medium cutlets of hake
3 tablespoons white wine OR 1 tablespoon vinegar with 2 tablespoons water OR little fish stock
1 large onion
3 large, skinned tomatoes
½ oz. butter or margarine
1 oz. grated cheese
1 oz. breadcrumbs (starch reduced)

1 Grease dish, then put in fish.
2 Season well and add wine, diluted vinegar, or fish stock.
3 Cover with VERY THINLY SLICED ONION, tomatoes, breadcrumbs and butter.
4 Cover with paper and bake for approximately 25–30 minutes in centre of a moderately hot oven (400°F.—Gas Mark 5).

Kippers in a colander

cooking time   6–8 minutes

This is one of the best ways to cook kippers since it keeps them very moist.

1 Stand a colander over a saucepan of boiling water.
2 Place kippers, or frozen kipper fillets, in the colander, cover with the pan lid and a wrapper if available.
3 Steam for 6–8 minutes.
4 Serve with any liquor which has been collected in the wrapper, poured over.

Herrings with onion stuffing

cooking time   6–8 minutes for grilling plus
                            15 minutes for cooking onions

you will need:

4 herrings	**To garnish:**
2 thinly sliced onions	sections of lemon
tomatoes	watercress
seasoning	
little fat	

1 Slice and simmer the onions in boiling salted water until tender.
2 Slit the herrings, clean well, fill with seasoned onion rings.
3 Make several slits in the fish.
4 Season fish and brush with little fat on the outside (if you are cutting down on fat, you can use very little as herrings have a high percentage of natural fat).
5 Cook for 6–8 minutes on the grid of the grill pan, with halved tomatoes in pan.
6 Garnish with lemon and watercress.

Jugged kippers

1 Put the kippers or kipper fillets into a big jug.
2 Pour over the boiling water and leave for several minutes.

Plaice and tomato pinwheels

cooking time   15–20 minutes

you will need:

4 large or 8 small plaice fillets	$\frac{1}{4}$ level teaspoon salt
1 dessertspoon mild mustard	8 small tomatoes, peeled juice of 1 lemon
2 tablespoons finely chopped parsley	$\frac{1}{2}$ level teaspoon powdered rosemary pepper

1 Skin fillets. Cut fillets in half lengthwise, and spread 1 side of each with mild mustard.
2 Wrap each half fillet around a tomato, the mustard side inwards.
3 Secure with tooth picks.
4 Arrange fillets in a greased, shallow baking dish and sprinkle with lemon juice, parsley, rosemary, salt and pepper.
5 Bake in a moderately hot oven (400°F.—Gas Mark 5) for 15–20 minutes.

Salmon mould

cooking time few minutes for heating aspic jelly

you will need:

8–12 oz. flaked cooked salmon	1 level teaspoon powder gelatine
$\frac{1}{4}$ pint mayonnaise (page 45)	2 tablespoons milk
$\frac{1}{4}$ pint aspic jelly	seasoning
2 hard-boiled eggs	2 sliced gherkins

1 When making the aspic jelly, dissolve the extra teaspoon powder gelatine in the liquid.
2 Allow to cool, then mix with the mayonnaise, milk, flaked salmon and 1 of the chopped hard-boiled eggs and 1 of the gherkins.
3 Season well.
4 Put into a rinsed mould and allow to set.
5 Turn out and decorate with the other egg and gherkins.

Plaice or sole whirls

cooking time   20 minutes

you will need:

4 large or 8 small fillets or fish	**Stuffing:** 2 large tomatoes
	$\frac{1}{2}$ oz. butter
Sauce:	2 hard-boiled eggs
2 tablespoons milk	2 teaspoons chopped parsley
$\frac{1}{2}$–1 oz. butter	
seasoning	parsley, for garnish

1 Skin and chop tomatoes, add hard-boiled chopped eggs, chopped parsley and butter.
2 Mix thoroughly and season well.
3 Spread on fish and roll.
4 Put into dish with the milk, butter and seasoning, cover with buttered paper.
5 Bake for 15–25 minutes in centre of moderately hot oven (400°F.—Gas Mark 5).
6 Lift on to hot dish and garnish with parsley.

Plaice with mushroom and celery stuffing

cooking time   15–20 minutes

you will need:

8 small or 4 medium fillets of plaice	squeeze of lemon juice 2 oz. mushrooms
1 teaspoon chopped parsley	2 oz. celery seasoning
grating of lemon rind	little butter

1 Chop the mushrooms and celery very finely.
2 Mix with the other ingredients.
3 Spread on the well seasoned fillets of fish.
4 Roll firmly and put into a buttered dish covered with buttered paper and bake for 15–20 minutes in a moderately hot oven (400°F.—Gas Mark 5).

White fish mould

As salmon mould above but add a few drops anchovy essence.

Shellfish macaroni special

cooking time   20 minutes

you will need:

4 oz. quick cooking macaroni	8 oz. chopped shrimps prawns or crabmeat
1 crushed clove garlic	1 onion
2 tablespoons chopped parsley	4 tablespoons water
½ oz. butter	2 tomatoes

1 Cook macaroni. Drain.
2 Melt butter in saucepan and lightly fry crushed garlic and chopped onion.
3 Add tomatoes, water and parsley. Mix thoroughly and bring to the boil.
4 Stir in shellfish and macaroni.
5 Heat thoroughly. Serve.

Shrimp and tomato salad

cooking time   few minutes only

you will need:

¾ pint tomato juice	2 teaspoons lemon juice
¾ oz. gelatine	2 or 3 minced gherkins
dash of Worcestershire sauce	endive to garnish
	shrimps to garnish
½ pint picked shrimps (fresh, frozen or canned)	cucumber to garnish
	seasonings as required

1 Soften gelatine in 3 tablespoons cold water, then dissolve over heat.
2 Stir in half the tomato juice and mix until gelatine is dissolved.
3 Cool down with remaining tomato juice and add flavourings and seasonings to taste.
4 Stir in shrimps last.
5 When mixture shows signs of thickening, spoon into prepared individual moulds.
6 When required, turn out shapes on to a lettuce or endive-lined dish, garnish with more shrimps and cucumber.
7 Serve with salad dressing (page 44) and additional shrimps.

Smoked haddock in tomato juice

cooking time   30 minutes

you will need:

1 smoked haddock	1 small can tomato juice
½ onion	1 teaspoon Worcester-shire sauce
salt	
pepper	

1 Put the haddock into a casserole, sprinkle with the finely chopped onion, season and pour on the tomato juice and sauce.
2 Cook in a moderate oven (375°F.—Gas Mark 4) for 30 minutes.

Sole Florentine

1 Serving

cooking time   10 minutes

you will need:

1 good-sized fillet of sole	seasoning
small knob of margarine	grated cheese
little milk	
2 tablespoons cooked spinach	

1 Since the spinach has to be re-heated, care should be taken to under-cook it slightly.
2 Mash the spinach or put through a sieve or mincer, then mix with the milk, margarine and seasoning.
3 Put at the bottom of an individual dish.
4 Roll the sole, season, and put into the centre.
5 Sprinkle the cheese over the top together with a very little more margarine.
6 Bake for good 10 minutes near the top of a moderately hot oven (400°F.—Gas Mark 5).

Sole or plaice with prawns

cooking time   8–10 minutes

you will need:

4 small plaice or soles	4 oz. prawns or shrimps
very little milk	seasoning
butter	lemon juice

1 Heat the prawns or shrimps gently with a little milk and tiny knob of butter.
2 Meanwhile brush the grid of the grill pan with melted butter and also brush the well seasoned sole with butter.
3 Grill on the dark skin side until tender, turn and cook on the second side.
4 Garnish with the prawns, lemon and parsley.

Sole or plaice with tomato herb stuffing

cooking time   15–20 minutes

you will need:

8 small or 4 large fillets of fish	little butter
½ teaspoon fresh lemon thyme, finely chopped	4 medium tomatoes
	1 teaspoon capers
	seasoning

1 Skin and chop the tomatoes and mix with the other ingredients.
2 Spread on the fillets of fish and roll firmly.
3 Put into a buttered dish and top with buttered paper.
4 Bake for approximately 15–20 minutes in a moderately hot oven (400°F.—Gas Mark 5).

Sole with asparagus

1 Serving

cooking time   10 minutes

you will need:

1 or 2 fillets of sole	little lemon juice
1 small knob of margarine	4 asparagus tips, cooked
seasoning	until just tender
little milk	

1 Cut the stalks from the asparagus, leaving pieces about 1 inch in length.
2 Pound the rest of the stalks, adding lemon juice, and seasoning.
3 Put into the fillets and roll tightly.
4 Steam with the margarine and milk between 2 plates over boiling water.
5 Drain and garnish with the tips.

Sole with rosy sauce

cooking time   10–15 minutes

you will need:

1 or 2 fillets sole	1 large tomato
$\frac{1}{4}$ pint white wine (Graves preferably) or juice of lemon and water	seasoning
	1 teaspoon finely chopped parsley

1 Skin the tomato and simmer for a few minutes with the white wine.
2 Put in the fish, together with the seasoning, and cook steadily for 3–5 minutes.
3 Drain the fish on to a hot plate, then put tomato stock through a sieve.
4 Reheat and pour over fish.
5 Serve with chopped parsley.

Soused fish

2 Servings

cooking time   45 minutes

you will need:

2 cutlets of fish or fillet of cod or fresh haddock	1 teaspoon sweet spice
1 small onion	2 tablespoons water
1 good teaspoon pickling spice	2 tablespoons vinegar
1 teaspoon sugar	$\frac{1}{4}$ teaspoon salt
	2 bay leaves

1 Put all the ingredients into a casserole.
2 Bake for 45 minutes in a very moderate oven.
3 This is good cold with a salad, or serve hot.

Stuffed crabs and mushrooms

cooking time   25–30 minutes

you will need:

4 oz. mushrooms	canned crab meat
2 oz. butter	1½ tablespoons lemon juice
½ teaspoon salt	1 teaspoon capers
2 tablespoons milk	1 teaspoon chopped parsley
2 egg whites, stiffly beaten	
2 medium-sized fresh crabs or equivalent in	

1 Sauté the mushrooms and butter and cook for 5 minutes.
2 Add seasonings and milk and heat for another 2–3 minutes.
3 Stir in crab meat etc., adding the stiffly beaten egg whites at the end.
4 Put either into the 2 shells or 4 individual dishes and bake in a moderate oven (375°F.— Gas Mark 4) for 20 minutes.

Stuffed hake cutlets

cooking time   20 minutes

you will need:

4 hake cutlets	mushroom and parsley stuffing (page 60)
salt and pepper	lemon and parsley to garnish
tomatoes	
1 oz. margarine	

1 Put the hake cutlets into a baking dish, sprinkle each piece of fish lightly with salt and pepper.
2 Divide the stuffing between the 4 cutlets, spreading this over the tops so that you completely cover the fish.
3 Rub the well greased greaseproof paper over.
4 Bake just above the centre of the oven in a moderate oven (375°F.—Gas Mark 4) for about 20 minutes.
5 Serve garnished with rings of lemon and parsley and baked tomatoes.

To dress a crab

no cooking

1 One medium-sized crab is enough for 2 people, 1 large one for 4 people. Feel the crab when you buy it and if it feels surprisingly light for its size, ask the fishmonger to break it open. 'Lightness' often indicates that it is 'watery' and you are not getting good solid crab meat.
2 Open the main part of the shell by pulling up the rounded part.
3 Take out the skin-like 'bag' and the greyish-brown fingers, both of which should be discarded.
4 Remove all white meat and mix with the meat from the claws.
5 Remove the brown meat and keep this separately.

Tomato and fish

1–2 Servings

cooking time   15–20 minutes

you will need:

2 small fillets of plaice, sole or whiting	3 mushrooms
2 large tomatoes	seasoning
	parsley

1 Remove centre from tomatoes.
2 Chop pulp finely then mix with chopped mushrooms, parsley and seasoning.
3 Put this mixture on the fillets, roll them tightly, then press into seasoned tomato cases, put tops back to keep fish moist.
4 Bake for 15–20 minutes in a moderately hot oven (400°F.—Gas Mark 5).

Tomato fish moulds

cooking time	few minutes

you will need:

½ pint tomato juice	2 tablespoons water
juice ½ lemon	4 tablespoons flaked
1 saltspoon salt	cooked white fish
1 rounded dessertspoon	cooked baked beans
gelatine	cucumber, radishes

1 Soften gelatine in the water.
2 Add very hot tomato juice and flavouring, stir until blended.
3 Leave until cold and then add flaked fish.
4 Pour into fish moulds (lightly oiled) and leave until firm.
5 Turn out and serve with baked beans and salad to taste.

Tomato whiting

cooking time	20 minutes

you will need:

4 whiting	4 tomatoes
lemon and parsley to	little lemon juice
garnish	seasoning

1 Clean the whiting and split down the centre.
2 Season well.
3 Fill with half the sliced tomatoes, top with the rest of the tomatoes, cover with buttered paper and bake for 20 minutes in a moderately hot oven (400°F.—Gas Mark 5).
4 Serve garnished with lemon and parsley.

Trout baked in cider

cooking time	25 minutes

you will need:

trout	seasoning
enough cider to cover	

1 Clean fish and put into buttered dish.
2 Pour over cider to cover. Season. Put greased paper on top.
3 Bake for approximately 25 minutes in moderate oven until fish is tender.
4 Lift on to a hot dish and serve.

Trout meunière

cooking time	10–15 minutes

you will need:

4 trout	juice of ½ lemon
4 oz. butter	parsley
salt and pepper	

1 Heat butter in large pan.
2 Fry the fish steadily in this. When cooked lift on to a hot dish.
3 Add lemon juice and seasoning to pan and cook until butter is golden brown.
4 Pour over fish and sprinkle with chopped parsley.

White fish turbans

cooking time	10 minutes

you will need:

white fish fillets	lemon and sliced
lemon juice	tomatoes to garnish
seasoning	

Steamed white fish fillets (whiting, plaice, sole, codling), look and taste more appetising curled as turbans.
1 Season the skinned and filleted fish and sprinkle with lemon juice before steaming in a covered colander (if you haven't got a real steamer) over just boiling water for 10 minutes.
2 Drain well, curl into turbans. These can be held in place if necessary with a toothpick headed by a piece of mushroom.
3 Garnish with lemon and sliced tomatoes.
4 Serve with cooked vegetables.

Whiting portugaise

cooking time	20–30 minutes

you will need:

4 whiting (each cut into	1 onion
2 fillets)	2 or 3 tomatoes
1 oz. butter	1 oz. grated cheese
salt and pepper	

1 Fold fillets in halves and place in a greased fireproof dish.
2 Slice onion very thinly and place on the top with sliced tomatoes.
3 Sprinkle over salt and pepper and grated cheese.
4 Put small pieces of butter on top.
5 Bake for 20–30 minutes in moderate oven (375°F.—Gas Mark 4).
6 Take care not to over-cook the fish, for whiting is very easily dried.

Seasonings and flavourings to improve your diet

Celery salt is a MUST in your store cupboard. Use a good pinch in savoury dishes, add a little to scrambled eggs occasionally, put into stews and soups —particularly when celery is not obtainable. Raw cauliflower dusted with celery salt is excellent as a salad ingredient.

Garlic salt. If you are not sure whether you will like the flavour of garlic then buy garlic salt. A pinch added to salad dressing gives you a faint taste of garlic. Put it into most savoury dishes and into a stew—particularly when onions are being used.

Paprika pepper. This is NOT a hot pepper but a sweet red pepper. It is excellent as a garnish, sprinkled on top of sauces or any savoury dish where colour is desired.

Cayenne pepper. This is the very hot pepper so be careful when using it— a little goes a long way. Add to some vegetable dishes to give a really 'hot' flavour. Use very sparingly as a garnish.

Mustard. A little made mustard put into cheese dishes helps to accentuate the cheese flavour.

French mustard should be served with steaks, mixed grill, etc. It is also an excellent basis for salad dressings.

Meat and Poultry

Cooking meat for slimmers

Lean meat is of great importance in your diet for it will provide the basic of your main meal. Obviously the best methods of cooking are roasting and grilling. Frying can be considered if you are allowed a certain amount of fat on the diet, but be very careful not to use an over-generous amount of coating or fat. You can have the meat from stews providing it is not covered with a really thickened gravy. As you will see from the calorie chart on page 84 some offal is listed. Liver in particular is very lean, but at the same time it is fairly high in calories.

Baking and roasting

If you have been in the habit of putting quite a lot of fat over your meat when roasting, you will find that most diets do not recommend this. You will, however, keep meat, poultry etc., beautifully moist without the use of fat if you wrap them well in foil before cooking. Chicken will need a little fat over the breast but, even so, if you melt this, brush it well into the flesh and wrap in foil you will find you can cut down appreciably on the amount generally used.

Cooking chops

Most chops, and in particular mutton or pork, have a good deal of fat on them. I think you will find you have a better flavour if you grill the chop with the fat and then cut most of this off before serving. If you cut the fat off before you cook it them you will find that the meat tends to be rather flavourless.

Grilling

It is extremely wise to use your grill when trying to lose weight, for you avoid having to add a great deal of extra fat and yet you do produce a good result. Rather than put pieces of fat on steak etc., brush with a little melted fat or oil. You will be surprised to find how much less you are using.

Low calorie gravy to serve with meat

A large helping of thickened gravy will often make the difference between your meal being a slimming one and it being a meal in which you lose no weight so watch this very carefully. If you slightly under-cook meat you will find when it is carved there is enough juice running from it to provide moisture. If, however, you must have a gravy then use less dripping and less flour than usual.

There are a number of casserole dishes in this book because we need a casserole, not only to eke out the meat, but also to provide a warm, satisfying dish in cold weather. You can either thicken it in the usual way and make sure your portion is served without any liquid, or you can cook the meat, vegetables etc., in a non-thickened stock. Take out your portion and thicken the rest for other people.

Meat is also very pleasant served with a good mushroom or tomato sauce. Recipes for these are to be found on page 44.

4 low calorie stuffings

A stuffing in meat serves two purposes. It gives an additional flavour and it helps rather expensive meat to go further.

Because most stuffings have a high percentage of breadcrumbs, fat etc., you will be well advised to leave these out from your diet or to replace the usual recipes with special slimming ones, such as the following:

1 Try an ordinary veal stuffing, but cut down the amount of fat and use chopped celery in place of the breadcrumbs.

2 Chopped mushrooms and tomatoes combined together, and seasoned and flavoured with herbs are an excellent stuffing for most meats.

3 Instead of sage and onion stuffing to serve with pork, boil onions, chop and mix with a little powdered sage.

4 Goose or duck, which by the way are not ideal to serve on a diet, are very good stuffed with whole peeled apples. If you have to eat goose or duck, avoid the rich fatty skin.

Grilled steak

cooking time   4—8 minutes

1 Brush grid and steak with butter or olive oil.
2 Season steak and, if wished, break down tissues by 'banging' with rolling pin or meat tenderiser.
3 Put on to grid of grill pan, with tomatoes and mushrooms at bottom of pan.
4 Cook rapidly on either side. This is sufficient for people who like their steak 'rare' (under-done) in the centre, but if you like it well done, lower the heat and cook steadily.
5 Garnish with watercress, but you could add dash Worcestershire sauce, and asparagus tips.

Curried steak rolls

cooking time   approximately 2 hours

you will need:

4 slices thinly cut buttock steak (about 3 oz. each)	2 good tablespoons chopped mushrooms
2 onions	1 tablespoon chopped parsley
1 oz. butter or margarine	about $\frac{3}{4}$ pint brown stock (or water plus beef bouillon cube)
1 level tablespoon curry powder	
little brown roux* to thicken	1 teaspoon concentrated tomato purée
	$\frac{1}{2}$ clove garlic

*To make brown roux combine 1 oz. fat with 1 oz. flour. Cook the flour in the melted fat until brown, but do not allow to burn. A small amount of this added to soups and stews will thicken them. It is particularly useful when only one person in the family is slimming, as a small quantity can be made, kept a day or so and used as required. In this way you can serve the same recipe, thickened for the rest of the family, unthickened for the slimmer.

1 Trim the steak and beat out thinly between 2 sheets of greaseproof paper.
2 Skin and chop onions finely.
3 Melt the butter in a small pan, add onions and fry gently until they are soft but not browned.
4 Stir in the finely chopped garlic, curry powder, parsley, mushrooms and seasoning.
5 Divide this mixture into 4 and spread over the 4 slices of meat.
6 Roll up and tie neatly with string. Fry in a little hot fat to seal on all sides.
7 Place in a stewpan or casserole. Add the stock and a close-fitting lid. Cook gently until tender (about 1½—2 hours).
8 Dish up the steak rolls in a hot entrée dish, remove string.
9 The liquid can be thickened for the *non-slimmers,* as below. Make the sauce by boiling up the liquor until reduced to about ½ pint. Add a little brown roux or a little flour blended with a few tablespoons of stock. Stir till boiling. Add the tomato purée and continue cooking until the sauce will lightly coat the spoon. Check the seasoning. Pour over the steak rolls.
10 Serve with creamed or mashed potatoes and a green vegetable.

Seasoned roast beef

8—10 Servings

cooking time
      1 hour 40 minutes to 2 hours 15 minutes

you will need:

4—5 lb. wing rib of beef   made mustard

Stuffing:

4 oz. mushrooms	2 tablespoons starch-reduced breadcrumbs
4 oz. celery	
4 tablespoons parsley	$\frac{1}{2}$ teaspoon dry mustard
1 small onion	salt and pepper
1 egg	

1 Have your butcher remove the bone and fillet from the joint, and cut a pocket through the meat parallel to the bone.
2 Spread the inside of the pocket with made mustard.
3 Finely chop all stuffing ingredients.
4 Combine them and blend well.
5 Stuff the joint.
6 Secure the open end with skewers or sew with thread.
7 Roast in very moderate oven (350°F.—Gas Mark 3) for 20—25 minutes per lb. and 20—25 minutes over or a little longer for well done beef.

NOTE: A thick slice of topside cut with a pocket and stuffed and slowly baked or braised is excellent.

Bourbon beef stew

cooking time   2½ hours

you will need:

1½ lb. stewing steak	little black pepper
1 oz. fat	2 carrots
1 clove garlic	2 stalks celery
1 onion	1 leek
8 oz. tomatoes	about 8 oz. potatoes
¼ pint red wine	chopped parsley for garnish
2 tablespoons water	
½ level teaspoon salt	

26

Dice meat and toss in fat.
After browning the meat lift it out and put
into a casserole.
Skin, crush and chop the garlic very finely,
skin and slice the onion.
Sauté these in the pan in which the meat was
browned. Add to them the chopped tomatoes,
wine, water, salt and pepper.
Stir till boiling.
Cover and simmer about 20–30 minutes.
Prepare and slice thinly the carrots, celery
and leek.
Scatter these over the meat. Pour the tomato
mixture over and top with the potatoes,
peeled and cut into ¼-inch thick slices.
Cover with a lid and cook in a very moderate
oven (325°F.—Gas Mark 2–3) about 1½
hours. Remove lid. Brush potatoes with fat
and sprinkle lightly with salt.
Return to oven near the top and cook without
the lid for about another 30 minutes until
golden. Scatter chopped parsley generously
on top.

Steak Creole

cooking time   2–2½ hours

you will need:

–1¼ lb. stewing steak	several sticks celery
2 onions	2 or 3 mushrooms
small packet frozen	2 oz. margarine
peas	¾ pint water or stock
oz. flour	seasoning
red or green pepper	

Heat the fat and fry the steak in this.
Lift out meat and add the sliced onions and
cook gently.
Add the stock and return meat to pan. Season
well, bring to boil, add the diced pepper,
celery and mushrooms.
Simmer gently for 2¼ hours.
Add peas towards end cooking time and
thicken gravy for non-slimmers.

Beef with olives

cooking time   2–2½ hours

you will need:

1 lb. stewing beef	3–4 carrots, sliced
seasoning	1 clove garlic
1 oz. fat or tablespoon oil	2 tablespoons red wine
4 oz. mushrooms, sliced	½ pint stock or water
4–6 small onions	few black olives

Cut the meat into small pieces.
Brown in the hot oil or fat in a pan.
Remove the meat and put it into a casserole.
Add onions, carrots and garlic, sliced mush-
rooms, the wine and stock.

5 Pour over the meat in the casserole, cover
lightly and cook in a slow oven (300°F.—
Gas Mark 2) for about 2–2½ hours.
6 Just before serving, add the olives and correct
the seasoning.
7 The liquid can be thickened at the end of
cooking for the non-slimmers.

Beef galantine

cooking time   2 hours

you will need:

1 lb. minced stewing beef*	8 oz. sausage meat
1 egg	2 tablespoons stock, or
salt and pepper	when not available milk
pinch dried mixed herbs	mustard

*When buying ready-minced beef see that it has not become dry on
the outside and has not a high proportion of fat and gristle.

1 Stir the minced beef into the sausage meat,
then add all the other ingredients, mixing
thoroughly with a fork.
2 Either press the mixture into a well-greased
basin or form it into a roll and put into a piece
of linen cloth.
3 Steam the galantine for 2 hours.
4 Turn out and cool. Cut into neat slices to
serve.

Individual meat loaves

cooking time   40 minutes

you will need:

1 lb. good quality minced beef	1 level teaspoon salt
1 tablespoon chopped parsley (or dried herbs to taste)	4 tablespoons fine dry starch-reduced breadcrumbs
¼ level teaspoon pepper	**To baste:**
1 egg	¼ pint tomato juice, canned or fresh
2 tablespoons chopped onion	2 teaspoons Worcestershire sauce
2 teaspoons made mustard	1 teaspoon made mustard

1 Blend the beef, lightly beaten egg, parsley,
onion, mustard, salt, pepper and breadcrumbs.
2 Form into 4 small oblong loaves and place
on a shallow baking pan.
3 Blend the tomato juice and seasonings and
spoon over the loaves.
4 Bake in a moderate oven (375°F.—Gas Mark
4) about 35–40 minutes.
5 Halfway through baking baste with liquid in
pan.
6 If preferred make into 1 loaf and cook for
about 1¼–1½ hours in very moderate oven
(350°F.—Gas Mark 3) basting 2 or 3 times
during cooking.

Beef darioles

cooking time   30 minutes

you will need:

12 oz. minced uncooked beef	1 tablespoon starch-reduced breadcrumbs
2 small skinned tomatoes	1 tablespoon milk
2 eggs	seasoning

1 Cut the tomato into slices and pound until a purée.
2 Mix with the beef, breadcrumbs, milk and seasoning, finally add the eggs. If desired the yolks only could be used and the whites kept for something else.
3 Put into 8 greased dariole tins and cover with greased paper.
4 Steam for 30 minutes.
5 Serve with brown gravy or tomato purée and mashed potatoes.

Featherweight shepherds pie

2–3 Servings

cooking time   15–20 minutes

you will need:

2 tomatoes	1 level teaspoon curry powder
1 sliced onion	pinch mixed herbs
8 oz. minced cooked beef	2 egg yolks
1 tablespoon oil or 1 oz. fat	$\frac{1}{2}$ gill stock
seasoning	pinch salt, pepper
2 egg whites	

1 Fry the onion and tomatoes and meat in the oil or fat until tender.
2 Add the seasoning, curry powder and cook for a further minute.
3 Add the egg yolks with stock and heat for a minute or two without boiling.
4 Put into a pie dish and cover with the topping.
5 To make the topping whisk the egg whites and seasoning until stiff.
6 Pile on top of the meat and bake for about 15–20 minutes in a moderate oven (375°F.—Gas Mark 4) till the meringue is golden brown.

Brisket of beef

4–5 Servings

cooking time $2\frac{1}{2}$ hours

you will need:

piece of beef about 3–4 lb.*	4 small onions
4 small carrots	good pinch pepper, mustard

*It is a good idea to buy enough brisket to allow for a cold meal for it is delicious with salad.

1 Soak the beef in COLD water for an hour or 2. If the butcher says it is very salty, soak overnight.
2 Put the beef into a large saucepan with the vegetables and half cover with cold water.
3 Add a good pinch pepper and mustard. Bring quickly to the boil.
4 Remove any scum that comes to the top. Put the lid on the saucepan, lower the heat and simmer gently, allowing about 30 minutes to each lb. and 30 minutes over, e.g. a 4 lb. piece will take $2\frac{1}{2}$ hours to cook. Do not thicken the liquid.
5 To serve the meat put on to a large hot dish with the vegetables and stock round and a few freshly cooked vegetables.

Slimming goulash

2 Servings

cooking time $1\frac{1}{2}$ hours

you will need:

either 4 oz. each stewing steak and veal OR 8 oz. stewing steak	small can tomatoes
	1 teaspoon paprika pepper
$1\frac{1}{2}$ oz. dripping or margarine	1 onion
	watercress and lettuce
	1 gill water

1 Cut meat into small pieces.
2 Heat fat in pan, add sliced onion, paprika pepper, meat, tomatoes and water. Add a little salt.
3 Put lid on pan and simmer for $1\frac{1}{2}$ hours.
4 Look into pan from time to time, and if necessary add a little water, but this should be a thick stew.
5 Serve with green salad.

Stuffed mutton chops

cooking time   15–20 minutes

you will need:

4–8 mutton chops	2 tablespoons finely chopped celery
2 tablespoons chopped onion	1 tablespoon chopped parsley
2 tablespoons fresh starch-reduced breadcrumbs	seasoning
	egg yolk

1 Split the lean part of the chops lengthwise.
2 Mix the onion and celery, breadcrumbs and parsley.
3 Bind with the egg yolk and fill the chops.
4 Secure the cut side with wooden cocktail sticks and grill.
5 Serve with boiled celery.

avarin of lamb

cooking time   1½ hours

you will need:

lb. lamb	1 clove of garlic
3 carrots	1 teaspoon mixed herbs
turnip	½ pint water and
onion	1 teaspoon meat extract
seasoning	OR ½ pint stock

Cut the meat into neat pieces.
Dice the carrots and turnip and onion and crush the garlic.
Put all the ingredients into a casserole and sprinkle the herbs over.
Add the water and the meat extract or stock, season well and bake in a moderate oven (375°F.—Gas Mark 4) for about 1½ hours.

Lancashire pie

4-5 Servings

cooking time   1½ hours

you will need:

lb. of middle neck of lamb	1 oz. butter
onion, sliced	1 lb. cooked carrots
lb. cooked potatoes	8 oz. cooked green peas
salt and pepper	a little grated cheese

Trim and cut the meat into neat pieces and bring to the boil in salted water.
Skim the surface of the water then add the onion and simmer for about 1 hour. If possible remove the meat from the bones.
Grease a deep pie dish with half the butter.
Put in the mashed carrots, with meat on top.
Add the peas and seasoning and cover with the sliced potatoes, overlapping like tiles on a roof. Dot with the remaining butter and scatter with cheese.
Bake in a hot oven (425°F.—Gas Mark 7) for about 30 minutes to heat all the ingredients.
Thicken about ½ pint of the lamb stock with a little flour or gravy thickening, if you prefer brown gravy, and serve with the pie.
Take out your portion and be VERY SPARING with the potatoes.

Lamb and tomato baskets

Servings

no cooking

you will need:

large tomatoes	4 oz. skinned grapes
lb. lean cooked lamb	sprigs of mint
teaspoon chopped mint	salad dressing (page 44)
tablespoons sweet corn kernels (canned or cooked)	juice of ½ lemon
	cucumber
	salt, pepper

1 Cut the tops off the tomatoes, scoop out the pulp and drain the hollowed cups.
2 Season well with salt and pepper.
3 Put the lamb through a medium cutter on a mincer, or chop finely, then mix with the sweet corn, mint and de-seeded grapes.
4 Bind with the lemon juice and salad dressing.
5 Fill the tomatoes with this mixture and garnish with either sprigs of mint or grapes.
6 Serve with thin slices of cucumber.

Lamb cutlet with green salad and marrow espagnole

1 Serving

cooking time   15 minutes

you will need:

1 large or 2 small cutlets (removing excess fat)	little chopped raw red or green pepper
lemon juice	lettuce
seasoning	

Marrow espagnole:

2 slices marrow	tomato
½ oz. margarine	1—2 mushrooms
piece onion	

1 Grill or fry cutlet.
2 Mix little chopped red pepper with lettuce and toss in lemon juice and seasoning.
3 Steam slices of marrow and while they are cooking make this thick sauce:
4 Heat margarine in pan. Add very little grated or chopped onion, the chopped skinned tomato and the chopped mushrooms.
5 Cook until soft, adding enough water or clear brown stock to moisten.
6 Season well.
7 Pile on top of the marrow.

Jellied lamb

cooking time   few minutes to dissolve aspic

you will need:

6—8 slices cold cooked lamb	2 hard-boiled eggs
1 packet aspic crystals	salt
1 heaped teaspoon gelatine	lemon juice
1 lb. cooked sliced green beans	

1 Dissolve the aspic in a pint of hot water.
2 Soften gelatine in a tablespoon cold water. Stir into aspic while hot.
3 Mix until fully dissolved.
4 Add lemon juice and salt.
5 When mixture begins to thicken cover the bottom of a dish.
6 Put in the lamb, eggs and cooked beans.
7 Spoon aspic over the top.
8 Serve with lettuce, tomato and cucumber salad.

Grilled fillet of veal

cooking time   10 minutes

1 Brush the veal with very little melted margarine or butter and season well.
2 Put under a hot grill and cook quickly on either side, then lower heat and cook more gently through to the centre.
3 Serve with lemon and a big plate of colourful Harlequin salad (page 40).

Liver, fried or grilled

cooking time   8 minutes

1 When frying or grilling liver do remember that it should never be overcooked, otherwise instead of being moist and tender it becomes hard and dry.
2 Fry with bacon or brush with very little melted butter and grill.
3 Allow 2–4 minutes either side depending on thickness.

Liver casserole

2–3 Servings

cooking time $1\frac{1}{4}$ hours

you will need:

$\frac{1}{2}$ teaspoon fat	$\frac{1}{2}$ pint stock
8 oz. liver	1 teaspoon tomato purée
2 onions	seasoning
2 mushrooms	

1 Melt the fat in a casserole, toss the liver in it and cook slightly.
2 Cut the onions into small pieces and add to the liver, then add the stock, tomato purée, mushrooms and seasoning.
3 Cook in a moderate oven (375°F.—Gas Mark 4) for $1\frac{1}{4}$ hours.

Baked liver loaf

cooking time   40 minutes

you will need:

1 lb. ox liver	1 onion
2 slices wholemeal bread	1 egg
1 level teaspoon salt	$\frac{1}{4}$ pint milk
good sprinkle of pepper	1 teaspoon made mustard

1 Simmer liver in salted water for about 10 minutes.
2 Drain and mince liver with the onion and bread.
3 Add the egg, slightly beaten, milk, salt, pepper and mustard.
4 Place in small well greased loaf tin. Stand in a pan of hot water.

5 Bake in a moderate oven (375°F.—Gas Mark 4) for 30 minutes.
6 Serve hot with green vegetables or cold with salad.

Onions stuffed with kidneys

cooking time   2 hours

you will need:

4 large onions	$\frac{1}{2}$ pint good brown stock
4 lambs' kidneys	seasoning

1 Cut thick slice from top of each onion and remove centre from each.
2 Chop this centre finely and add to stock, season.
3 Pour this into a casserole.
4 Stuff a seasoned kidney into each onion, put in casserole and cover the onions with the thick slices from the top, to keep kidneys moist.
5 Put lid on casserole and cook for 2 hours in centre of a very moderate oven (350°F.—Gas Mark 3).

Kebabs for slimmers

This is a most attractive way of serving grilled food and, providing you use little fat in basting, not too high on calories.

1 Arrange a mixture of foods (kidneys, bacon, sausages, diced steak or tender lamb, mushrooms, tiny onions, tomato halves, pineapple cubes, etc.) on metal skewers.
2 Brush with plenty of melted butter and cook under the grill, turning the skewers to make sure that the food is well cooked.
3 The food can be slipped from the skewers quite easily on to serving plates.
4 Serve with vegetables or cooked rice.
   The pineapple cubes should be used sparingly on a slimming diet unless you have fresh pineapple.

Savoury kebabs

cooking time   10–15 minutes

you will need:

4 frankfurter sausages, halved	4 mushrooms
	4 bacon rashers, halved
4 thick slices onion	2 tomatoes, quartered

1 Wrap each halved frankfurter in half a bacon rasher, secure with wooden picks.
2 Thread each of 4 greased skewers with an onion slice, then alternate pieces of frankfurter and tomato, end with a mushroom.

rush contents of each skewer with little
elted butter and place under grill turning
ten and brushing with more butter for
)–15 minutes or until ingredients are
ooked.

Devilled chicken casserole

cooking time   1½ hours

you will need:

small chicken (about 2 lb.) cut in pieces	1 dessertspoon dry mustard
onion, chopped	2 or 3 tomatoes, chopped
teaspoon paprika	1 medium green pepper, chopped
about ¼ pint hot water	1 level teaspoon salt

Rub chicken pieces all over with dry mustard.
Place chicken, chopped tomatoes, green
pepper and onion in a casserole.
Stir the paprika and salt into the hot water
and pour over the other ingredients.
Cover and cook slowly, either in a saucepan
on top of the stove or in a casserole in a very
moderate oven (325–350°F.—Gas Mark
2–3) for about 1½ hours.

Steamed chicken

cooking time   1½ hours

you will need:

a small chicken	salt and pepper
¼–½ pint milk or stock	a blade of mace

Joint the chicken and place it in a basin or
top of a double saucepan with the milk or
stock and seasonings.
Cover, place over hot water and cook for
1½ hours, until the chicken is tender.
The milk can be used for egg sauce (page 43).

Chicken stew

cooking time   approximately 1½ hours

you will need:

1 chicken (about 2 lb.)	1–2 oz. butter
2 onions	pinch of cayenne pepper
1 clove garlic	2–3 tablespoons milk or yoghourt
4 skinned tomatoes	1 tablespoon oil
seasoned flour	
seasoning	

Simmer giblets for stock.
Cut chicken into 4 joints and sauté them in
the oil until lightly browned on all sides.
Lift out the chicken and put the chopped
onion into the pan, together with the finely
chopped garlic. Add the tomatoes, roughly
chopped and a little seasoning. Bring to boil.
Place chicken joints in stewpan or casserole
with the tomato mixture. Gradually add

a little hot stock to the tomato mixture to
just cover chicken. Add a pinch of cayenne
pepper and salt and pepper.
5 Cover and simmer very gently until tender
(about 1–1½ hours according to quality of
chicken).
6 Stir in milk or yoghourt just before serving.
7 Serve with green salad.

Grilled chickens

There is a very plentiful selection of young
chickens available which are excellent for
grilling. These can be jointed, brushed with
a very little fat and cooked under the grill
for approximately 20 minutes until tender.

Piquant chicken grill

cooking time   approximately 20 minutes

you will need:

2 small chickens (about 1½ lb. each)	pepper
	salt
2 tablespoons mild mustard	1 oz. butter, melted
1 tablespoon lemon juice or tarragon vinegar	

1 Have the chickens split in half and sprinkle
them with pepper and salt.
2 Place under a hot grill for 3 minutes each
side.
3 Remove from heat and spread over them the
mild mustard blended with the lemon juice
or vinegar and butter.
4 Grill under medium heat, turning several
times, until the flesh is white and tender,
10–15 minutes.
5 Baste with any drippings from the pan.

Chicken mould

cooking time   few minutes

you will need:

1 lb. minced cooked chicken	1 pint chicken stock*
	little lemon juice
1 teaspoon powdered gelatine	2 hard-boiled eggs (not essential)
seasoning	

*If the chicken stock is not rich enough to form its own jelly you
will need 1–2 level dessertspoons powder gelatine to the pint stock,
depending on the richness of the chicken liquid.

1 Soften the gelatine in a very little cold chicken
stock then dissolve in the very hot stock.
2 Add the lemon juice, seasoning, sliced
hard-boiled eggs and chicken.
3 Put into mould and allow to set.

Devilled chicken

1 Serving

cooking time 8 minutes

you will need:

4–6 oz. cold cooked chicken	pinch of cayenne pepper
1 teaspoon tomato ketchup	½ teaspoon black pepper
1 teaspoon vinegar	1 teaspoon made mustard
	1 tablespoon olive oil

1 Cut the chicken into neat pieces.
2 Blend all the other ingredients together, brush over the chicken.
3 Grill until browned on both sides.
4 Serve with boiled rice and sweet chutney.

Chicken mousse

cooking time

10 minutes to thicken egg yolks etc.

you will need:

12 oz. minced cooked chicken	2 teaspoons powdered gelatine
2 gills chicken stock	3 eggs
	seasoning

1 Beat the egg yolks over hot water until slightly thickened.
2 Dissolve the gelatine thoroughly in the chicken stock, then add to egg yolks, together with seasoning and chicken.
3 When cold fold in the stiffly beaten egg white.
4 Put into small individual dishes.
5 Serve with finely shredded lettuce.

Savoury loaf

cooking time few minutes to dissolve jelly

you will need:

8 oz. minced or diced chicken	chopped parsley
2 chopped hard-boiled eggs	8 oz. minced ham or bacon
	1 pint aspic jelly

1 Mix the ham with one third of the jelly which should be cold but not set.
2 Put this in the bottom of a loaf tin.
3 When firm add the egg, mixed with another third of the aspic jelly and finally add the chicken and jelly.
4 When fully set turn out the loaf by dipping the tin in hot water.

Turkey with sour sweet sauce

cooking time 40 minutes

you will need:

approximately 12 oz.– 1 lb. cooked turkey cut into neat pieces	2 saccharine tablets or sugar substitute
½ pint white wine or cider	seasoning
4 large tomatoes	2 or 3 pieces of celery
	1 teaspoon capers

1 Put the wine, sliced tomatoes, chopped celery seasoning, saccharine, capers into a saucepan
2 Simmer about 20 minutes, add the turkey and continue simmering for 20 minutes.
A good way of serving already cooked turkey.

Pigeons in cider

cooking time approximately 2 hours

you will need:

2 pigeons	8 oz. tomatoes
2 oz. butter	1 level teaspoon salt
½ pint dry cider	little black pepper
¼ pint stock or water	chopped parsley

1 Split the pigeons in half through the back and toss in the hot butter.
2 Put into a casserole.
3 Pour the cider and stock or water into the pan in which the pigeons were browned, and bring to the boil.
4 Add the chopped tomatoes, salt and pepper Simmer for 10 minutes.
5 Rub through a sieve. Pour over the pigeons Cover closely and simmer for 1½–2 hours.
6 Scatter chopped parsley over, and serve.

Turkey and asparagus mould

3–4 Servings

cooking time few minutes to heat aspic

you will need:

6 oz. cooked turkey	½ pint aspic jelly
1 small can asparagus or 1 bundle fresh cooked asparagus	lettuce
	watercress

1 Cut the turkey into neat pieces and cut the asparagus stalks into a suitable size for the individual moulds.
2 Set a little aspic jelly in each mould and put 3 or 4 heads of asparagus in the bottom.
3 Cover with more aspic jelly, then set slices of turkey on this.
4 Repeat this, until all the asparagus stalks and turkey are used up, then leave to set.
5 Turn the mould out on to a bed of lettuce and watercress.

Turkey ring mould

cooking time few minutes to heat aspic

you will need:

¾ pint aspic jelly	4 oz. minced cold ham or boiled bacon
seasoning	lettuce, watercress
chopped parsley	sliced tomatoes
sliced cucumber, radish	
8 oz. minced cold turkey	

repare aspic.
Decorate a border mould with sliced cucumber and radish.
Add the chopped ham and minced turkey to the aspic jelly with the chopped parsley and seasoning.

4 When the mixture is beginning to set pour it into the mould, leaving in a cool place to set and when it is quite firm turn it out on to a glass dish.
5 Fill the centre with lettuce, watercress and sliced tomato.

Diet food should be interesting food

As stated in my introduction, I have not intended to offer any special slimming diets in this book, but simply to give you helpful recipes. I have tried to make all of them as interesting as possible to both taste and look at, in order to avoid monotony, to keep you feeling well fed, and to prevent you from becoming bored with your diet.

Obviously when you embark upon any diet it means sacrificing a lot of your personal likes and dislikes. However, if you approach the diet in the right frame of mind, that is—you ARE going to stick to it, you ARE going to like it— then it helps enormously.

If you have been in the habit of having rather rich sauces and gravies to flavour food, you will miss these a great deal. Instead, you must learn to make full use of fresh and dried herbs and various seasonings.

A few suggestions are given on page 24.

Salads and Sauces

Salads—6 ways they can help your diet

One of the main difficulties of slimming for someone with a rather large appetite is that they feel they are having so little to eat. You are therefore very fortunate if you like salads, because they help enormously to give variety and a feeling of being well fed. Here are a few ways of using them to the best advantage:

1 As well as serving salad as a cold dish, a good substantial salad is an excellent idea with a HOT meal. It makes a more interesting dish, and also helps to take the edge off your appetite. I think you will find some of the combinations of salad greens suggested on this page very nice to serve with hot dishes as well as cold.
2 The look of food is just as important in a slimming menu as any other. On this page you will find suggestions for attractive vegetable garnishes to 'dress up' your rather plain diet.
3 Many people forget that a really thick mayonnaise adds a great deal of calorie value to a salad. So if you are slimming seriously, avoid rich mayonnaise or a lot of oil. Choose one of the low-calorie dressings on pages 44–46 or moisten your salad with a little lemon juice, vinegar or tomato juice.
4 Tomatoes and cucumber are both extremely low on calories, so include plenty of these with your salads.
5 Above all else, avoid monotony, for it is with salads that you can have infinite variety.
6 One of the drawbacks of a serious slimming diet is that you have to cut out a lot of the interesting puddings, sauces and so on, but you can learn to replace these with gay, colourful, appetizing salads.

Remember, success in salad making depends on:

1 Fresh, crisp ingredients.
2 Careful washing in running water if possible.
3 Complete removal of moisture after washing. Place in a salad basket or clean tea towel and shake vegetables (out of doors for preference), using a smooth swinging movement.
4 Tear lettuce apart, never cut with a knife.
5 Add colour and variety by using tomatoes, raw grated carrot, beetroot, hard-boiled eggs, grated apples, stoned plums or dates.
6 Flavour with herbs. Parsley should be added just before serving. A few leaves of mint, sage, thyme, dill or chives can all be used raw in small amounts, to add flavour to salads.

Mixed green salads

Green salads may be mixed, marinated and served in the same wooden, glass or china bowl. Or the greens may be arranged on salad plates and served with French dressing (page 45) or one of the other dressings (pages 44–46). For a suggestion of garlic or onion, rub bowl with a freshly cut surface of either. Greens are always crisp and chilled. The French break greens in pieces. Greens may also be cut in quarters, smaller pieces, or shredded, according to type. Toss together lightly with a large spoon and fork, or two forks. Use one of the following combinations of vegetables:

1 Lettuce and watercress.
2 Lettuce, curly endive, spinach.
3 Lettuce, romaine, and endive.
4 Lettuce, watercress, chicory, sliced green pepper.
5 Lettuce, sliced cucumbers and radishes, green pepper rings.
6 Lettuce, chicory, endive, chopped onion and garlic.
7 Curly endive, chopped pimento.
8 Chicory, endive, tomato sections.
9 Sliced radishes and cucumbers.
10 Chopped pimento, green peppers, green and black olives.
11 Dandelion leaves, watercress, sliced radishes.
12 Dandelion leaves, chicory, garlic and diced crisp bacon.

Crisp vegetables, garnishes

Carrot straws: Wash and scrape or peel tender young carrots and cut in quarters, then in small strips, or cut in narrow strips about 3 inches long. Place on plate, cover with damp cloth and chill for 1 hour before serving.
Celery curls: Select large tender stalks of celery, cut in 3-inch lengths and slit each lengths in narrow parallel strips almost to the end. Place in water, add a quantity of chipped

ice. As the slit celery chills, the ends will curl. If desired, cut both ends of celery almost to centre of piece and when chilled both ends will curl.

Chicory: Select the tender white leaves from the heart. Wash and crisp in ice water. Serve as salad.

Onion rings: Select large, mild onions, Bermuda or Spanish onions are good. Cut in thin slices crosswise and place in ice water. When thoroughly chilled and crisp, loosen rings with a fork and drain well. Serve on relish dish with carrot strips, radish roses or other crisp vegetables.

Radishes: Select firm radishes with unwilted leaves. Wash or scrub thoroughly, cut off tails on root ends and blemishes, if any, then rinse. Wrap in cloth and place in refrigerator for 1–2 hours or until crisp and cold.

Radish roses: Select firm round radishes, uniform in size, with no blemishes, wash and cut tops leaving about 1 inch of stem on each. Cut a thin slice from root end of each. With a sharp thin knife, cut uniform thin strips of the red peel almost through to the stems. Place radishes in ice water. As they chill, the peel will curl back like petals.

American prawn salad

no cooking

you will need:

4 oz. peeled prawns	1 level tablespoon salad
salt and pepper to taste	dressing (page 44)
4 sticks celery	2 eating apples
2 teaspoons oil	lettuce
2 teaspoons vinegar	

1 Blend the oil and vinegar with the seasoning and mayonnaise, add the prawns, celery and 1 apple cut into dice, mix well together.
2 Serve the salad on a bed of lettuce leaves and garnish with the remaining apple cut into wedges.

Apple and ham luncheon salad

no cooking

you will need:

6–8 eating apples	4 tablespoons light cream
juice of 1 lemon	or top of milk
1 lb. cooked ham	2 oz. crumbled blue
2 oz. green pepper or	cheese
celery	¼ pint salad dressing
fresh parsley	(page 44)
Garnish:	
apple slices	lettuce

1 Cut balls from peeled apples, using melon-ball cutter or a sharp teaspoon, or cut into neat dice.
2 Soak apple balls in lemon juice to preserve colour.
3 Drain, and combine with diced ham and sliced celery or pepper.
4 Blend salad dressing and cream, add to apple mixture and toss.
5 Sprinkle with blue cheese and garnish salad with parsley and a star of red skinned apple wedges, dipped in lemon juice to keep colour bright.
6 Serve in lettuce-lined salad bowl.

Apple baskets

no cooking

you will need:

4 apples	4–6 oz. cottage cheese
2 oz. celery or chicory	lemon juice
few nuts	lettuce
seasoning	few dates

1 Cut a good slice off the top of each apple but leave the skin on.
2 Remove the core, then scoop out most of the apple and chop into neat dice.
3 Sprinkle the apple, including the 'shell', with lemon juice.
4 Mix the cheese, seasoning, chopped dates, chopped celery or chicory with the diced apple, and pile into the apples.
5 Replace the 'cap'. Serve garnished with lettuce.
6 Chopped nuts may also be added to the filling.

Aubergine salad

cooking time   10 minutes

you will need:

1 large aubergine	small quantity of oil or
2 sliced tomatoes	butter for cooking
2 sliced gherkins	aubergine
½ tablespoon oil	salad dressing (page 44)
seasoning	
lettuce	

1 Peel the aubergine, cut it into neat slices.
2 Heat the butter or oil in a frying pan and toss the aubergine in this until just soft but unbroken.
3 Cool, then toss in the salad dressing and seasoning.
4 Lay on the lettuce, and surround with sliced tomatoes and gherkins.

Avocado pear salad

no cooking

you will need:

2 avocado pears	small piece cucumber
1 small grapefruit	endive or lettuce
2 tomatoes	salad dressing (page 44)

1 Peel the avocado pears, remove the stones and cut the fruit into thin slices.
2 Put into a bowl with the sections of grapefruit and toss in salad dressing.
3 Make a bed of the lettuce or endive, pile the pear mixture in the centre and arrange rings of cucumber and tomato around.

Baked beans and bacon salad

cooking time   5–10 minutes

you will need:

2 rashers cooked bacon	2 tablespoons chopped
2–3 oz. baked beans	celery
	pickled onions

1 Cut fat from bacon if you are watching your diet very carefully.
2 Mix bacon and beans well, then add the celery, squeeze of lemon juice, a little chopped pickled onion.
3 Serve hot or cold. Baked bean are an excellent protein food and can be included in your diet when you are not having meat or fish.

Banana and cottage cheese salad

no cooking

you will need:

2 small bananas	3 tomatoes
1 teaspoon lemon juice	lettuce
4 oz. cottage cheese	watercress

1 Slice bananas, sprinkle with lemon juice.
2 Put lettuce into a bowl.
3 Pile watercress on to dish and then the cheese, in pyramids.
4 Slice the tomatoes and make outer ring of these with banana.

Bean salad

no cooking

you will need:

1 lb. cooked beans	lemon juice
2 hard-boiled eggs	2 oz. grated cheese
green pepper	

1 Drain cooked runner beans, season, and flavour with a little lemon juice.
2 Combine with chopped hard-boiled eggs, and thinly sliced green pepper.
3 Pile on lettuce leaves and sprinkle with grated cheese.

Bean-stuffed tomato salad

no cooking

you will need:

tomatoes	cooked or baked beans
celery	lemon juice seasoning
Worcestershire sauce	lettuce

1 Allow 2 tomatoes per person.
2 Remove centre pulp, chop finely, then mix with a little finely chopped celery, cooked beans, few drops lemon juice, dash of Worcestershire sauce.
3 Pile this into tomato cases.
4 Serve with lettuce.

Beef pyramid salad

no cooking

you will need:

8 oz. minced cooked beef	1 teaspoon oil
1 tablespoon	seasoning
Worcestershire sauce	beetroot
1 tablespoon chopped	lettuce
parsley	1 good tablespoon
4 small tomatoes	chutney or mustard
3 oz. sliced cucumber	pickle

1 Mix together the minced beef, Worcestershire sauce, parsley, two of the tomatoes, cut into slices, cucumber, oil and the chutney or pickle.
2 If using the latter chop it finely.
3 Season well. Put on to a bed of lettuce, form into a pyramid shape and garnish with rings of beetroot.

Cabbage and carrot salad

no cooking

you will need:

8 oz. cabbage	salt
3 carrots	salad dressing (page 44)

1 Mix shredded cabbage with carrots, salt and salad dressing.

Cabbage relish salad

no cooking

you will need:

8 oz. cabbage	1 tablespoon chopped
½ green pepper	spring onion
½ small cucumber	2 tablespoons salad
2 oz. celery	dressing (page 44)
1 tablespoon vinegar	seasoning

1 Combine cabbage, diced cucumber, diced green pepper, finely chopped celery and chopped onion, vinegar and salt. Mix lightly with fork.

2 Chill in refrigerator for 1 hour.
3 Just before serving add salad dressing.

Carrot and raisin salad

no cooking

you will need:

3 large carrots	2 oz. raisins
2 teaspoons chopped	salad dressing (page 44)
parsley	or lemon juice
lettuce	

1 Mix grated raw carrots with seedless raisins.
2 Add salad dressing to moisten.
3 Serve on lettuce, garnish with parsley.

Cauliflower and orange salad

no cooking

you will need:

celery salt	salad dressing (page 44)
seasoning	orange
cauliflower	celery or chicory
apple	

Cauliflower, either cooked or raw, is delicious in salads. In following recipe the salad is best if raw cauliflower is used.
1 For each person allow about $\frac{1}{4}$ of a small cauliflower.
2 Divide into tiny flowers and mix these with sections of orange, skinned and chopped.
3 Toss together, then add a little grated sweet apple, a little chopped celery, good pinch of celery salt, pepper.
4 Add enough of the dressing to moisten and, if wished, enough onion juice to give a 'bite'.
5 Serve with cheese or by itself.

Celery cole slaw

no cooking

you will need:

12 oz. cabbage	$\frac{1}{4}$ pint salad dressing
4 oz. chopped celery	(page 44)
	2 apples

1 Mix together the finely shredded cabbage heart (as crisp and fresh as possible), the finely chopped celery, the apples, grated or finely chopped.
2 Toss in the dressing.
3 Serve cold with lean meat, flaked fish or hard-boiled egg.

Cheese and carrot salad

no cooking

you will need:

2 oz. cheese	$\frac{1}{2}$ cucumber
2 or 3 carrots	1 lettuce
4 tomatoes	lemon juice

1 Grate the cheese and carrots and slice the tomatoes and cucumber.
2 Wash the lettuce and toss it in lemon juice dressing.
3 Arrange on dish.

Cheese carrot salad

1 Serving

no cooking

you will need:

1 large carrot	1 oz. cheese or cottage
2 tablespoons tomato juice	cheese
chicory	watercress
2 chopped olives	a little onion, crushed

1 Grate carrot.
2 Mix with chopped chicory, olives, tomato juice, onion, and the cheese (grated if you do not use cottage cheese).
3 Serve on watercress.

Cheese and grapefruit salad

1 Serving

no cooking

you will need:

$\frac{1}{2}$ large grapefruit	lettuce
1 tomato	1 oz. cheese
3–4 apple rings	

1 Remove pips from grapefruit, cut away fruit in sections.
2 On crisp lettuce, arrange rings of grapefruit, tomato and apple.
3 Grate cheese and pile on top.

Chicken salad Caprice

3–4 Servings

no cooking

you will need:

1 large ripe banana	3 tablespoons mayonnaise
2 tablespoons lemon juice	(page 45)
1 large orange	2 tablespoons thin cream
8–12 oz. cooked chicken	or yoghourt
meat	4 oz. black grapes
	crisp lettuce leaves

1 Slice the banana into a bowl and turn over and over in the lemon juice.
2 Peel the orange and add the segments, freed from skin and pips, to the bowl.
3 Add the chicken cut into $\frac{1}{2}$-inch dice, the mayonnaise and the cream or yoghourt.
4 Mix lightly, cover, and set aside in a refrigerator to allow the flavour to blend.
5 To serve, line a shallow bowl with lettuce leaves, pile the chicken salad in the centre and garnish with the halved and de-seeded grapes.

Chicken salad Véronique

no cooking

you will need:

12 oz. cooked chicken meat	¼ teaspoon grated lemon
6 oz. green grapes	rind
2 tablespoons salad oil	4 tablespoons thin cream
1 tablespoon lemon juice	2 ripe tomatoes
salt and pepper to taste	crisp lettuce leaves

1 Cut the chicken into small pieces and mix with the halved and de-seeded grapes.
2 Combine the oil, lemon juice and rind, seasonings and cream, then stir this dressing into the chicken and grape mixture.
3 Cover and set aside in a refrigerator to allow the flavours to blend.
4 To serve, line a shallow bowl with lettuce leaves, pile the chicken salad into the centre and garnish with thin wedges of tomato.

Cottage cheese and fruit platter

no cooking

you will need:

8 oz. cottage cheese	2 large crisp lettuce
2 red apples	leaves
8 peach slices, fresh or	1 tablespoon lemon juice
canned	about 4 plump prunes
	small bunch of grapes

1 Pile the cottage cheese in a large lettuce leaf, washed and shaken dry.
2 Core and slice the unpeeled apples, toss in lemon juice and arrange with the grapes on the platter with the cheese.
3 Place the other large prepared lettuce leaf on the platter and arrange the well drained peach slices and prunes on this.
4 No dressing is needed with this salad.

Cottage cheese moulds

no cooking

you will need:

½ pint tomato juice or milk	6 oz. cottage cheese or
seasoning	finely grated cheese
2 teaspoons chopped	2 teaspoons chopped
parsley	gherkins
2 dessertspoons powder	¼ pint water
gelatine	

1 Beat tomato juice or milk very gradually into cheese until smooth mixture.
2 Dissolve the gelatine in hot water.
3 Add the gelatine to the cheese with seasoning, parsley and gherkins.
4 Pour into 4 small moulds and when set turn out and serve with salad.

Cucumber cups with shrimps in mayonnaise

no cooking

1 Peel straight-sided cucumber and cut cross-wise into 1-inch lengths.
2 With end of potato peeler, scoop out one of the cut sides of each length to form little cups.
3 Mix peeled shrimps with a little mayonnaise (page 45) and lemon juice and put about 1 teaspoon of the mixture into each cup.

Egg stuffed tomatoes

you will need:

4 tomatoes	4 black olives
4 hard-boiled eggs	curly endive
2 tablespoons mayonnaise	

1 Wash the tomatoes and cut almost through three times (see cover picture). Discard seeds.
2 Chop the eggs and mix in the mayonnaise.
3 Fill the centre of the tomatoes with the egg mixture.
4 Top each tomato with a black olive.
5 Serve on a bed of endive.

Fish and cucumber salad

1 Serving

no cooking

you will need:

endive	2 oz. cucumber
chicory	2 oz. tomato juice
4 oz. white fish (cooked)	seasoning
	fennel, dill or parsley

1 Use 4 oz. cooked white fish per person.
2 Mix with chopped chicory and chopped cucumber.
3 Mix with tomato juice, seasoning, pinch of chopped fennel, dill or parsley and serve on endive.

Fish salad

cooking time   10 minutes

you will need:

1–1¼ lb. white fish	¼ pint salad dressing
1–2 hard-boiled eggs	(page 44)
a few shrimps or prawns	2–3 oz. chopped
to garnish (optional)	cucumber
salt and pepper	1 tablespoon vinegar or
	lemon juice

1 The most suitable fish for a salad are cod,

hake, halibut, skate (particularly good), turbot or fresh haddock. Flat fish such as plaice and whiting are rather unsuitable, for they do not flake easily.

2 Put the fish in a steamer, add a good sprinkling of salt and pepper and cook over a pan of boiling water until the fish comes away from the bone and seems quite soft. The time required varies according to the thickness of the fish, but test after about 10 minutes. If you do not possess a steamer, then cook in about ½ pint water, with seasoning.

3 Meanwhile soak cucumber for about 30 minutes in the lemon juice or vinegar.

4 When fish is cold, combine with salad dressing, cucumber and chopped egg white.

5 Pile on a bed of lettuce, decorate with the chopped egg yolk and for special occasions garnish with a few shrimps or prawns.

Fish salad

cooking time   10–15 minutes

you will need:

1 lb. white fish	small onion
sliced cucumber to garnish	diced cucumber
2 hard-boiled eggs	diced beetroot
2–3 oz. chopped celery	mayonnaise (page 45)
or chicory	

1 Cook fish gently (do not overcook), flake it and mix with diced cucumber, chopped celery, chopped onion, mayonnaise.

2 Garnish with sliced cucumber and beetroot, and serve with green salad.

Fish and apple salad

no cooking

you will need:

cooked white fish	apple
lettuce	lemon

1 Flake fish, mix with equal quantity of diced dessert apple and serve with crisp lettuce.

2 Serve with wedges of lemon.

French tomato salad

no cooking

you will need:

tomatoes	parsley
shallots or onions	French dressing (page 45)

In France they use a much larger tomato, but English tomatoes are perfect this way.

1 Select large ripe tomatoes and slice them evenly.

2 Chop finely some shallots or onions, chop a little parsley and scatter both over the tomatoes.

3 Marinate with French dressing and serve very cold.

Fresh tomato ring

cooking time   10 minutes

you will need:

1 pint fresh tomato pulp*	bay leaf
1 clove garlic or 1 chopped	clove
onion	salt and pepper
½ teaspoon celery salt	hot water
½ oz. gelatine	salad
cheese or meat	

*Made by simmering 1¼ lb. tomatoes and ¼ pint water.

1 Cook the tomato pulp with flavourings and seasonings and, when well flavoured, rub through a coarse sieve.

2 Dissolve gelatine in the water and mix all together with cooked tomato pulp.

3 Put into a border mould and allow to set.

4 Turn out by dipping quickly 2 or 3 times in hot water.

5 Serve with fresh green salad and diced cheese or meat in centre of ring.

Frosted cheese salad

no cooking

you will need:

8 oz. cream cheese	seasoning
½ gill milk	mayonnaise (page 45)
apple rings	lettuce

1 Mix cream cheese with milk.

2 Add seasoning and mayonnaise to taste.

3 Put into freezing tray and leave until lightly frosted.

4 Serve with rings of apple on a bed of crisp lettuce.

Green and red pepper salad

no cooking

you will need:

1 sweet red pepper	Special French dressing
1 green pepper	(see page 45)
2 oz. mushrooms	6 black olives

1 Wash the peppers and remove pips. Slice thinly.

2 Wash the mushrooms and slice thinly.

3 Arrange in a dish and pour over the Special French dressing.

4 Garnish with black olives.

Golden asparagus salad

1 Serving

no cooking

you will need:

6 asparagus heads, cooked (either canned, fresh or frozen)
1 hard-boiled egg
lettuce or watercress
low calorie salad dressing (page 45)
seasoning

1 Carefully cut hard-boiled egg into 4 thick slices.
2 Remove yolk, put a little aside for garnish and pound remaining yolk until smooth, adding seasoning to taste.
3 Put asparagus heads through egg white rings, arrange on bed of crisp lettuce or watercress and pour over a little of the dressing, top with seasoned egg yolk mixture.
4 Sprinkle with plain egg yolk.

NOTE: Frozen asparagus heads can now be obtained. You will find them delicious and surprisingly economical.

Harlequin salad

1 Serving

no cooking

you will need:

2 oz. sprouts or cabbage
1 or 2 sprigs cauliflower
little celery
½ sliced apple
1 small grated carrot
½ oz. grated cheese
paprika pepper
2 slices of orange

1 Shred sprouts or cabbage and arrange on flat plate.
2 Put small 'heap' of carrot, then chopped celery.
3 The cauliflower should be topped with the cheese.
4 The apple, orange and paprika pepper are arranged round.

Hot Russian salad with cheese

cooking time   20 minutes

you will need:

mixed vegetables*
tomato juice
cheese

*If you have been advised to cut down on root vegetables, replace these with cauliflower, onions, sprouts.

1 Use as large a mixture of vegetables as possible—carrots, swedes, turnips, beans, peas.
2 Dice and cook, season well then drain and bind with tomato juice.
3 Pile on hot plates and cover with grated cheese.

Ham and cheese salad

no cooking

you will need:

4 oz. diced cooked ham
4 oz. diced Dutch cheese
2 tomatoes
little chopped chives or spring onion
lettuce

1 Arrange lettuce on flat dish.
2 Mix ham, cheese and quartered tomatoes together.
3 Moisten with a low calorie dressing (page 45) and pile on to lettuce.

Mint and grape salad

no cooking

you will need:

grapes
lettuce
mint
cucumber
salad
lemon juice
orange

1 Arrange halved grapes on lettuce leaves with wafer thin slices of cucumber and orange.
2 Mix chopped mint with little lemon juice and seasoning and pour over salad.

Moulded meat salad

cooking time   10—15 minutes

you will need:

½ pint clear meat stock or canned consommé
4 tomatoes
2–3 oz. sliced cucumber
8 oz. cooked meat, cut into neat pieces
1 large onion
1 slightly rounded dessertspoon powder gelatine
2 pieces of celery
1 carrot
bay leaf
parsley

1 Put the onion, celery, carrot and bay leaf into the stock and heat gently for a few minutes, then let it stand an hour or so to absorb the flavour of the vegetables.
2 Take them out and dissolve the powder gelatine in the stock. Remember it is easier to dissolve if you soften it in a tablespoon of cold stock before pouring on the rest of the stock, which should be very hot.
3 When the jelly is cold, add the diced meat, sliced cucumber and tomatoes.
4 Put into a rinsed mould and allow to set.
5 Turn out and garnish with parsley.

Nut and celery salad

no cooking

you will need:

1 oz. nuts
watercress
celery
banana
salad dressing (page 44)

1 Wash a small bunch of watercress, peel a banana and cut into thin slices.
2 Wash and trim a head of celery and cut into small pieces.
3 Chop shelled nuts coarsely.
4 Mix all ingredients well together and serve with salad dressing.

Orange and shrimp salad

no cooking

you will need:

4 oranges	1 diced hard-boiled
1 pint shelled shrimps	egg
1 gill low calorie dressing	2 small, raw grated
(page 45)	carrots

1 Cut top off oranges or halve.
2 Take out pulp and toss with shrimps in dressing with carrot.
3 Pile into orange cases and garnish with chopped egg.

Pear salad

no cooking

you will need:

4 large fresh pears	1 oz. chopped nuts
juice of 1 lemon	2 tablespoons chutney or
4 oz. grated or cottage	mayonnaise (page 45)
cheese	4 tomatoes
4 oz. cooked peas	lettuce
hard-boiled egg, sliced	cucumber

1 Peel and core the pears, steep in the lemon juice.
2 Fill pear centre with a mixture of the cheese, nuts and peas.
3 Top with a little chutney and a wedge of tomato.
4 Serve on a bed of lettuce with cucumber, egg and the remaining tomato.

Red cabbage and celery salad

no cooking

you will need:

½ raw red cabbage	2 tablespoons yoghourt
3 oz. shredded celery	4 diced black olives
1 rounded dessertspoon	salt, pepper, mustard
grated Spanish onion or	to season
chives	cabbage lettuce leaves
4–6 eating apples	

1 Mix the cabbage with the celery and the onion or chives.
2 Fold in the yoghourt, black olives, salt, pepper and mustard.
3 Fill into hollowed-out eating apples and stand on curly cabbage lettuce leaves.
4 Chill before serving or serve in salad bowl.

Pineapple and cream cheese salad

no cooking

you will need:

fresh pineapple	lettuce
chopped walnuts	cucumber
cream cheese	

1 Cut the pineapple into rings.
2 Arrange on crisp lettuce.
3 Fill the centre of each pineapple ring with cream cheese and top with chopped walnuts.
4 Serve with sliced cucumber.

Prawn tomato salad

no cooking

you will need:

4 large tomatoes	4 oz. prepared prawns
seasoning	2 hard-boiled eggs
watercress	lettuce

1 Halve tomatoes and scoop out centre pulp.
2 Mix pulp with prawns, chopped egg, seasoning.
3 Pile back into tomato cases.
4 Serve with watercress and lettuce.

Raw cauliflower salad

no cooking

you will need:

sliced celery heart	seasoning
chopped red sweet	cauliflower flowerets
pepper	salad dressing
sweet pickles	onion juice

1 Slice thinly crisp, uncooked cauliflower flowerets, and marinate in salad dressing (page 44) for 30 minutes.
2 Drain, add remaining ingredients and mix thoroughly.

Raw vegetable salad

no cooking

you will need:

½ small cabbage*	2 tomatoes
2 carrots	watercress
1 small young turnip	oil and vinegar
1 medium sized raw	to taste
beetroot	seasoning

*Any other raw vegetables in season may be included—instead of cabbage. Raw Brussels sprouts, spinach or cauliflower may be used.

1 Shred the cabbage and grate the other vegetables.
2 Slice the tomatoes.
3 Arrange in an attractive design on flat dish and add seasoning and dressing to taste.

Red and green pepper salad

no cooking

you will need:

2 green peppers	2 tablespoons salad
1 red pepper	dressing (page 44)
4 oz. grated cheese	2 chopped gherkins
seasoning	2 large tomatoes
	lettuce

1 Cut a piece off one end of each of the green peppers and scoop out the centre seeds.
2 Mix the grated cheese (or cream cheese if preferred) with the salad dressing, chopped red pepper, gherkins, sliced tomatoes, the pieces of green pepper (cut finely) and seasoning.
3 Pack this into the centre cavity of the green peppers.
4 Using a sharp knife cut the peppers into slices across and arrange the rings on a bed of lettuce.

Stuffed tomato and meat salad

no cooking

1 As stuffed tomato fish salad (see this page) but substitute cooked meat for fish, and Worcestershire sauce for anchovy essence.
2 A little crushed garlic can be added.
3 To lamb, add a very little chopped mint, to chicken, a little chopped rosemary or dill, to beef add a very little grated horseradish.

Summer salad

no cooking

you will need:

1 teacup stoned cherries	2 tablespoons salad
½ teacup sliced strawberries	dressing (page 44)
1 teacup redcurrants	1 teacup white currants
	½ teacup blackcurrants

1 Mix together all the fruit with the dressing.
2 Put in small heaps on a bed of lettuce.
3 This is especially good with lamb or cold duck.

Savoury crab salad

2–3 Servings

no cooking

you will need:

1 large dressed crab	1 teaspoon chopped
5 oz. cooked rice	parsley
lettuce	2 teaspoons chopped
1 dessertspoon lemon	gherkins
juice or vinegar	1 tablespoon oil
2–3 oz. finely chopped	seasoning
celery	lettuce

1 Mix together all ingredients except the lettuce.

2 Season well.
3 Serve on individual dishes on a bed of lettuce. Garnish with small claws of the crab.

Sea island salad

no cooking

you will need:

1 can corn	2 tablespoons grated
6½ oz. can tuna	onion or chopped
lettuce	spring onion
olives	1 tablespoon pickle or
1 hard-boiled egg	chutney
2 tablespoons chopped	2 tablespoons mayonnaise
parsley	(page 45)

1 Combine drained corn with tuna and onion, parsley, pickle relish.
2 Toss with mayonnaise.
3 Arrange on bed of lettuce.
4 Decorate with olives and egg.

Water lily lamb salads

cooking time   25 minutes

you will need:

3 or 4 globe artichokes	salad dressing (page 44)
8 oz. cooked lamb	capers
pepper	lettuce
salt	radishes

1 If possible soak the artichokes in salted water for about 2 hours before cooking.
2 Cook in boiling salted water for approximately 25 minutes, or until sufficiently tender to pull out the leaves easily.
3 Drain artichokes and allow to cool.
4 Trim the bottoms of the stems, so they stand easily, and remove the centre leaves, leaving a row of 2 leaves round the outside. Remove the hairy 'choke' so that the bottoms only are left.
5 Fill the centre of the artichoke 'baskets' with finely diced lamb moistened with salad dressing.
6 Garnish with the capers. Serve the leaves that have been pulled from the artichokes as a border round the dish and put the artichokes on a bed of lettuce. Top with rings of radish.
7 Serve extra salad dressing to accompany the additional artichoke leaves.

Stuffed tomato and fish salad

1 Serving

no cooking

you will need:

milk	1 dessertspoon cucumber,
2 tomatoes	chopped
2 oz. cooked fish	parsley, chopped
watercress	few drops anchovy
	essence

1 Remove centre pulp of tomatoes, chop finely, then mix with flaked white fish, a little chopped parsley, seasoning, anchovy essence and chopped cucumber.
2 Pile into tomato cases.
3 A little milk can be added to make moister filling.
4 Serve with watercress.

Turkey and ham salad

no cooking

you will need:

4 oz. cooked turkey	2 eating apples
4 oz. cooked ham	mayonnaise (page 45)
6–8 tablespoons of diced fresh pineapple and melon	lettuce tomato diced cucumber

1 Dice the turkey and ham, mix with the pineapple and melon.
2 Core the apples without peeling, slice thinly and add to salad, then mix with mayonnaise.
3 Arrange the lettuce on a serving dish and pile the salad on top.
4 Garnish with tomato and cucumber.

Virginia chicken salad

3–4 Servings

no cooking

you will need:

2 medium size dessert apples	8 oz. cooked diced chicken meat
3 tablespoons lemon juice	4 sticks celery, sliced
4 tablespoons cream	1 tablespoon walnuts, chopped
2 tablespoons salad dressing	crisp lettuce leaves
$\frac{1}{4}$ teaspoon salt	small red skinned apple sprigs parsley

1 Peel and core the apples, cut into $\frac{1}{4}$-inch dice and toss with 1 tablespoon lemon juice.
2 Lightly whip the cream and stir it into the salad dressing, salt and 1 tablespoon lemon juice.
3 Add the diced apple, chicken, celery and nuts.
4 Mix, cover and set aside in a refrigerator.
5 To serve arrange the lettuce leaves around a flat dish and pile the chicken salad in the centre.
6 Cut the unpeeled red skinned apple into slices and dip in the remaining lemon juice.
7 Garnish the salad with the apple slices and parsley sprigs.

Waldorf salad

no cooking

you will need:

4 dessert apples	lettuce or endive
$\frac{1}{4}$ pint mayonnaise (page 45)	$\frac{1}{4}$ pint yoghourt
	2–3 oz. chopped celery
few grapes	few chopped walnuts

1 Peel and chop $2\frac{1}{2}$ apples, mix with the celery, grapes and nuts.
2 Blend mayonnaise with yoghourt.
3 Toss apple well in this dressing.
4 Arrange bed of lettuce or endive at bottom of dish then pile mixture on top.
5 Decorate with thin apple slices.

Sauces for slimmers

Most diets tell one to avoid sauces, particularly very rich ones and this, of course, is very wise for you are adding with the butter, the flour, the milk and even cream contained in a sauce, a considerable amount of food value to the dish.

It may be that you are one of the people who cannot enjoy fish, etc. without a sauce, in which case the following egg sauce, and the other sauces based on it, are lower in calories than the standard white or béchamel sauce.

Egg sauce

cooking time

10–15 minutes very slow cooking

you will need:

1 egg	$\frac{1}{3}$ pint milk
seasoning	$\frac{1}{2}$ oz. butter

1 Put the egg, milk, butter and seasoning into the top of a double saucepan or basin over hot water.
2 Whisk or stir briskly until thick enough to coat the back of a wooden spoon. Take great care the water never boils vigorously otherwise the sauce will curdle.

Variations:

Anchovy sauce

As above, but whisk in $\frac{1}{2}$–1 teaspoon anchovy essence when the sauce has thickened.

Caper sauce

As above, but add 1–2 teaspoons of capers plus 2 teaspoons vinegar when the sauce has thickened.

Cheese sauce

As above, but blend $\frac{1}{2}$–1 teaspoon of made mustard with the egg and milk before cooking. When the sauce has thickened add 1–2 oz. grated Parmesan cheese or 4 oz. grated Cheddar cheese.

Mock hollandaise sauce

As above, but use 1 oz. butter which should be added gradually when the egg and milk has thickened. Whisk in 2 teaspoons of lemon juice or vinegar.

Parsley sauce

As above, but add approximately 1 tablespoon of chopped parsley when the sauce has thickened.

Prawn or shrimp sauce

As above, but add 2 oz. chopped cooked shrimps or prawns when the sauce has thickened. If using fresh shrimps or prawns you can make a stock by simmering the shells and use half fish stock and half water.

Tip to dieters

You will cut down on the calorie count of a sauce if, instead of all milk, you use $\frac{1}{2}$–$\frac{2}{3}$ vegetable stock. You can choose either a white or béchamel sauce or the egg sauce (page 43).

Mushroom sauce

cooking time   10 minutes

you will need:

4 oz. mushrooms   seasoning
$\frac{1}{4}$ pint water

1 Chop the mushrooms very finely.
2 Simmer in the water until tender.
3 Rub through a sieve.
4 Thin down if required.

Onion sauce

cooking time   15 minutes

you will need:

1 lb. onions $\frac{1}{4}$ oz. butter
seasoning $\frac{1}{3}$ pint water

1 Chop onions and simmer in water until soft.
2 Rub pulp through sieve.
3 Reheat with seasoning and butter, adding extra water if too thick.

Sweet-sour sauce

no cooking

1 Mix equal quantities of diabetic redcurrant jelly and French or mild mustard.
2 Delicious with veal or lamb or grilled cuts.

Tomato sauce

cooking time   25 minutes

you will need:

1 lb. halved tomatoes   1 chopped onion
seasoning   1 chopped apple
$\frac{1}{4}$ pint water   pinch mixed herbs

1 Simmer all the ingredients together until the tomatoes are very soft.
2 Rub through a sieve. Do this firmly to make sure the pulp of the tomato, apple and onion are pushed through to thicken the sauce well.
3 If necessary thin with a little stock or water.
4 To give a more spicy flavour to the sauce you can add a crushed clove of garlic or a little Worcestershire sauce or a bouillon cube.

Salad dressings for slimmers

If you can eat a salad with just lemon juice or vinegar it is, of course, more slimming than any other way but many people find it is quite uninviting and it is therefore better to add just a little dressing. On the following pages you will find recipes that are lower in calories than usual.

Salad dressing

no cooking

you will need:

2 tablespoons milk   1 tablet saccharine,
2 tablespoons lemon juice   crushed
    or vinegar   good pinch salt and
mustard   pepper

1 Mix milk with lemon juice or vinegar.
2 Add seasoning, saccharine and blend thoroughly.
This gives flavour and moisture to rather dry salads.

Special French dressing

no cooking

you will need:

½ tablespoon salt	a pinch of sugar or
¼ teaspoon pepper	¼ saccharine tablet
¾ teaspoon mustard	2 tablespoons vinegar
	1 tablespoon olive oil

1 Mix the seasonings and sugar with the vinegar.
2 Gradually add the oil.
3 Mix well just before serving.

Low-calorie yoghourt dressing

no cooking

you will need:

1 small jar (¼ pint) yoghourt	1 teaspoon lemon juice
½ saccharine tablet, crushed or sugar substitute	1 tablespoon French mustard
	1 tablespoon finely chopped parsley or capers or gherkin

Blend all ingredients well together.
Excellent for a chicken or meat salad.

Variations on basic dressings

Tomato salad dressing

no cooking

you will need:

¼ pint thick tomato purée, made from good 8 oz. tomatoes	pinch salt, pepper sugar
2 tablespoons yoghourt or milk	½ teaspoon made mustard squeeze lemon juice or vinegar

1 Skin tomatoes and if very firm heat for a few minutes with little water. If soft, this is not necessary.
2 Rub through a sieve and mix with the rest of the ingredients.

Garlic dressing

no cooking

1 Add ½ clove or very finely chopped garlic, and, if liked, a teaspoon of finely chopped parsley to any of the salad dressings on pages 44 to 45.
2 Serve with crisp chicory, celery, endive and with ham.

Herb dressing

no cooking

1 Add a teaspoon of chopped parsley (or ½ parsley and ½ chervil) and a teaspoon of chopped chives with very little chopped lemon, thyme and sage, to any of the salad dressings on pages 44 to 45.
2 Excellent with all simple green salads and mixed vegetable salads.

Olive dressing

no cooking

1 Add 2 or 3 finely chopped green olives, 1 heaped teaspoon of chopped chives and 1 sieved hard-boiled egg yolk to any of the salad dressings on pages 44 to 45.
2 Excellent with fish and tomato salad.

Piquante dressing

no cooking

1 Add a rounded teaspoon of very finely chopped shallot and the same of chopped capers and gherkins to any of the salad dressings on pages 44 to 45.
2 Wonderful with potato salad or with salads or meat.

Hard-boiled egg mayonnaise

no cooking

you will need:

yolks of 2 hard-boiled eggs	2 tablespoons milk or thin cream
1 tablespoon vinegar or lemon juice	¼ teaspoon dry mustard powder
salt	pepper
½ saccharine tablet	

1 Rub the egg yolks through a sieve or pound until very smooth then add all the seasonings.
2 Gradually beat in the cream, then the vinegar and continue beating until very smooth.

Yoghourt dressing

cooking time   3 minutes

you will need:

2 egg yolks	1 dessertspoon made mustard
¼ pint yoghourt	

1 Warm yoghourt, beat in egg yolks.
2 Cook slowly, stirring for 3 minutes.
3 Season further to taste.
4 Serve cold. For cucumber, coleslaw and fish salads.

Mint dressing

no cooking

1 Add a teaspoon of finely chopped mint to any of the salad dressings on pages 44 to 45.
2 Good with cold peas or sliced green beans, French beans or cold lamb.

Yoghourt 1000 island dressing

no cooking

you will need:

¼ pint yoghourt	3 tablespoons finely
1 tablespoon chopped	chopped celery heart
olives or gherkins	1 finely chopped hard-
2 teaspoons	boiled egg
Worcestershire sauce	½ teaspoon finely
	chopped onion

1 Mix thoroughly and chill before serving.
2 Excellent with all salads.

Simple pickles and relishes for slimmers

Simple pickles help to make a meal more interesting and the following recipes are low in calories and therefore quite permissible on most diets.

Pickled cucumbers

no cooking

1 If the cucumbers are very small they can be left whole, but otherwise cut into convenient sized pieces.
2 Put into a brine made with 2 oz. salt to 1 pint cold water.
3 Soak overnight or cover with salt.
4 Boil vinegar and pickling spices together.
5 Allow to each pint of vinegar 1 level tablespoon mixed pickling spices.
6 Boil for 15 minutes, strain and cool.
7 Remove the cucumber from the brine, rinse well under the cold tap, then drain thoroughly.
8 Pack into jars, pour over the cold vinegar and seal carefully.

Savoury apples

cooking time   1 hour

you will need:

1 medium onion	salt and pepper
1 teaspoon chopped fresh	4 small baking apples*
sage OR ¼ teaspoon	(cored and peeled)
dried sage	½ oz. margarine
*Choose a rather sweet variety.	

1 Boil and chop the onion.
2 Mix sage, salt and pepper with the onion.
3 Place apples in a baking dish and press the onion mixture into the core cavities.
4 Add just enough water to cover the bottom of the dish.
5 Dot the apples with the margarine and bake them in a moderate oven till tender, but not broken.
6 Serve hot in the baking dish.
  Good with cold pork or bacon.

Pickled red cabbage

no cooking

1 Cut the cabbage into shreds.
2 Put into a basin with a good sprinkling of salt between each layer.
3 Leave for 24 hours.
4 Drain thoroughly, pack into jars and pour over the cold spiced vinegar.
5 For quantities of spiced vinegar see pickled cucumbers.

Apple chutney

cooking time   45 minutes

you will need:

2 lb. cooking apples	2 teaspoons powdered
12 oz. large onions	ginger
8 oz. seedless raisins	1 tablespoon salt
3 gills malt vinegar	½ teaspoon cayenne
4 saccharine tablets	pepper

1 Peel and core apples and peel onions.
2 Chop both finely with the raisins.
3 Add rest of ingredients and put into saucepan.
4 Simmer till the mixture is quite soft then add the saccharine tablets or sugar substitute.
5 Stir well and beat to a pulp.
6 When cold put into 1 lb. jars and cover securely.
7 This chutney is ready for use at once, or will keep for a long while.

Pickled onions or shallots

no cooking

1 Remove outer skins from the onions or shallots, using a stainless knife to prevent their discolouring.
2 Soak in the brine for 36–48 hours.
3 For quantities of brine see above as for pickled cucumbers.
4 Remove onions from brine and cover with COLD spiced vinegar.

15 ways to lose weight

1 This is most important of all. If you are trying to lose a lot of weight, under NO circumstances should you embark on a serious slimming diet, *without seeking the advice of your doctor.* If you only want to lose a few pounds, then no harm will be done if you just eat carefully. Don't try and lose enormous amounts of weight in a week. Tablets, etc., to help you slim, should again NEVER be taken except under medical advice.

2 Make up your mind you are going to enjoy following your diet and that it is not a penance.

3 Of the foods you are allowed, pick out the ones you like best and take a delight in making them look interesting.

4 If you are in the habit of eating meals quickly, try and slow down a little. This gives the illusion that you are, in fact, eating more.

5 Either make the plates look full up with salad, etc., or serve your meals on smaller plates.

6 When you have been given a diet by a doctor, or you are following it from any other source, don't be persuaded by kind friends to depart from it. Give it a really fair trial.

7 Try and plan your cooking to fit in with the family. They will enjoy many of the recipes, and you can easily give them larger helpings or add rather richer sauces and so on. It makes very hard work of a diet if you have to cook completely different meals for your family.

8 Don't be a fanatic about the calories you eat. If you do go out and are entertained, and eat a little more than you know you should out of politeness, then simply cut down on the next meal.

9 Whilst exercising does not reduce in the same way as diet, plenty of fresh air and exercise will keep you fit and make you feel better altogether.

10 Give yourself some kind of 'goal', either a rather special dress, or a present, at the end of the period of dieting.

11 Get your family to join in. By that I don't mean slim, unless they need it, but they CAN help you a great deal. For example—if your husband is in the habit of bringing you sweets, then ask him to choose a nice peach or some other attractive substitute.

12 Don't bore your friends and relations by talking about the diet from early morning till late at night.

13 AVOID ANYTHING BETWEEN MEALS. If you are feeling hungry don't reach for a biscuit or a piece of cake. Have a carrot or lettuce leaf instead.

14 If it is the men folk in the family who are dieting instead of you, try to produce some of their favourite meals made up in a slimming way. You could serve apple pie if you sweetened the fruit with saccharine and allowed them only a minute amount of pastry.

15 Don't feel you cannot go out to meals when on a diet. If you are eating in a restaurant it is more than likely that you can have roast beef or grilled fish, or meat served with salad instead of rather starchy vegetables. Have a clear soup and ask for fresh fruit or a small piece of cheese for your sweet course.

Savoury and Vegetable Dishes

5 breakfast tips for slimmers

It is very unwise to eat no breakfast if you are trying to lose weight for most people feel rather hungry in the middle of the morning and will then consume several sweet biscuits, and perhaps a milky coffee which does far less good than a well balanced breakfast and is far more fattening.

You have a wide variety of foods that you can serve for breakfast.

1 Start the meal with grapefruit, tomato juice or fresh fruit juice.
2 If you have been in the habit of serving a cereal, then be very sparing with this and with the milk you put on top.
3 It is, however, wiser to leave out the cereal and have a boiled egg, or a grilled rasher of bacon with tomatoes a poached egg or boiled haddock. Herring roes are another excellent choice for breakfast.
4 If you can't do without toast then make it a thin, crisp piece. Even better, get into the habit of having starch-reduced rolls or you can now buy starch-reduced bread from many bakers.
5 On page 79 you will find sugarless marmalade and this will give you a well balanced breakfast that is not too high in calories.

Cooking eggs for slimmers

Eggs are probably one of the most useful of all foods in a slimming diet for if you have boiled eggs, soft or hard, you add no extra calories in the form of butter, milk, etc. Below you will find suggestions for the best way of cooking scrambled, poached and fried eggs.

Fried eggs

Unless you have a very good griddle you will need enough fat to get the bottom of the pan really greased. Make sure this is very hot and then break in the egg. If you are using a griddle, rub it over with a pastry brush, dipped in oil. Heat for several minutes, then break the eggs on to it and cook in the usual way.

Poached eggs

You will have a more slimming poached egg if you lower the eggs into boiling salted water (with a few drops of vinegar), rather than poach them in cups or an egg poacher where you need a good knob of butter. Make sure the water really is boiling, stir rather vigorously to give a 'hole' in the centre, lower the egg into this part of the water and cook steadily.

Scrambled eggs

Most people like scrambled eggs with plenty of butter in the pan and possibly a little milk or cream mixed with the eggs. This tastes delicious but makes the egg into a more fattening food. The secret is to grease a basin at the bottom, stand this over boiling water, add the seasoned and well beaten eggs and cook slowly over the boiling water, stirring well.

Savoury dishes for slimmers

Quite often people who follow a diet most carefully spoil the effect of a day's well-planned dishes by having a sandwich snack, or a supper dish which seems light, but is, in actual fact, rather fattening.

If meat has been already included in your day's diet, then choose a savoury dish which contains eggs, cheese or plenty of vegetables, to give you a substantial and at the same time slimming meal.

In the following chapter you will find a great number of savoury dishes which use eggs, cheese and vegetables in very interesting ways. Quite a number of these contain cheese which CAN be included in your diet, if served in moderation. Cheese is particularly useful for a light supper, or for those people who are not big meat eaters as it is very nourishing, and contains a lot of protein.

Tip to dieters

Meat balls, Scotch eggs and so on can be included in your diet if, instead of frying them, you cook them in the oven. Scotch

eggs will take approximately 25 minutes in a moderately hot oven.
Simply grease the baking tin and turn them once or twice during cooking.

Baked eggs

cooking time   10–12 minutes

you will need:

4 eggs	seasoning
½ oz. butter	skimmed milk

Grease 4 individual baking dishes with the butter.

Break an egg into each, season well and cover with the milk.

Either bake slowly for about 10–12 minutes (350°F.—Gas Mark 3) until the eggs are just set or steam in a pan of hot water.

Variations: Add asparagus tips to eggs. Add a tablespoon of cooked mushrooms to eggs. Add a tablespoon chopped prawns to each egg.

Baked egg in tomato

cooking time   15 minutes

Scoop out the interior of a large firm tomato.

Break an egg into it, sprinkle with grated cheese, salt and pepper and bake in a moderate oven.

Benedict eggs

cooking time   7–10 minutes

you will need:

4 poached eggs	2 slices ham
4 slices starch-reduced bread	mock hollandaise sauce (page 44)

1 Toast the bread.
2 Grill the meat and place a slice on each piece of toast.
3 Place the poached egg on top of the meat and cover with sauce.

Cheesey scrambled egg

cooking time   10 minutes

you will need:

1 oz. margarine	4 eggs
2 tablespoons chopped ham	2 oz. grated cheese mushrooms to garnish

1 Melt the fat in a saucepan and scramble the eggs in the normal way.
2 When nearly cooked, add the chopped ham (or bacon) and grated cheese.
3 Pour into an oval earthenware dish and garnish with grilled mushrooms.

Creamed eggs and onion au gratin

cooking time   40 minutes

you will need:

1 lb. medium size onions	salt and pepper
parsley	little grated nutmeg
4–6 poached eggs	1 oz. grated cheese

1 Boil the onions until tender.
2 Chop and season, add nutmeg, heat well.
3 Put into small casseroles or a large dish.
4 Top with the eggs and cheese and put under very hot grill for 1–2 minutes.

Egg baskets

cooking time   10 minutes

you will need:

4 hard-boiled eggs	2 oz. mushrooms
1 oz. margarine	salt and pepper

1 Skin and chop mushrooms, fry them in margarine.
2 Cut eggs lengthwise, take out the yolks.
3 Mash the yolks and mix them with the mushrooms, add seasoning.
4 Keep the egg whites warm, fill with mushroom mixture.
5 Arrange stalks of parsley to look like handles.

Golden rod eggs

cooking time   10 minutes

you will need:

5 eggs	salt and pepper
½ pint tomato sauce (page 44)	asparagus tips
	mushrooms

1 Hard-boil the eggs and when they are cold slice three of them and chop the white part of the other two.
2 Add these to the sauce and season.
3 Put into a dish, add the eggs and sieve the other egg yolks over the top.
4 Serve with asparagus tips and grilled mushrooms.

Gruyère eggs

cooking time   10 minutes

you will need:

4 eggs	¼ pint stock
4 oz. Gruyère cheese	½ oz. margarine or butter
grated nutmeg	1 teaspoon chopped parsley
salt	1 teaspoon chives

1 Melt the cheese with the margarine, stock, salt and seasoning.
2 Add eggs, well-beaten, and stir until set.

Ile flôttante

cooking time   15–20 minutes

you will need:

2 eggs   grated cheese

1 Separate the whites and yolks of eggs, whisk the whites until stiff.
2 Place these in a lightly greased pie dish, place the yolks on top of the whipped whites, sprinkle with the cheese and bake in a very moderate oven (250°F.—Gas Mark 2) for 15–20 minutes.

Kippered eggs

cooking time   12 minutes

you will need:

2 eggs   pepper
2 kippers   2 tablespoons milk
1 oz. margarine   buttered toast

1 Cook the kippers in boiling water until tender.
2 When cool, take out the bones and sieve or mash the flesh.
3 Put this into a small pan with the milk, margarine and eggs, lightly beaten, season slightly with pepper.
4 Cook gently, stirring constantly until eggs thicken.

Omelettes

cooking time   5 minutes

To make a plain omelette

you will need:

$1\frac{1}{2}$–2 eggs per person   warm water
seasoning

1 Rub the omelette pan with oil or melt a little butter in this.
2 Get this really hot, pour in eggs and do not move until a very thin film has set at the bottom of the pan.
3 Work the omelette to enable it to cook quickly and be light.
4 The moment the omelette is set, put in the filling, and roll or fold away from the pan handle.

Variations:

Aux fines herbes: Add finely chopped herbs to the eggs before cooking.
Tomato: Stew tomatoes with seasoning in butter. Use some as a filling and the rest as a garnish.
Mushroom: Cook the mushrooms in little milk, add seasoning, add to eggs before cooking.

Ham: Either chopped ham is added to the eggs before cooking or mix the ham with very little milk.
Cheese: Put a layer of grated cheese through the middle before folding or fill with thick cheese sauce.
Chicken or other poultry: Heat in creamy sauce and use as filling.
Mixed vegetables: A mixture of softened peppers, mushrooms and tomatoes make a delicious filling. Simmer these together first.
Spinach: Spinach which should be sieved or well chopped is an excellent filling.

Poached eggs in jelly

cooking time   few minutes

you will need:

4 eggs   salad
$\frac{1}{2}$–$\frac{3}{4}$ pint aspic jelly

1 Poach eggs lightly as on page 48 and trim into neat shape.
2 Dissolve aspic jelly and put layer in mould.
3 Allow to set. Put eggs on top and cover with rest of jelly.
4 When quite firm unmould on to bed of salad.

Spanish eggs

cooking time   20 minutes

you will need:

4 large tomatoes   4 eggs
little melted fat   salt and pepper
2 onions   parsley to garnish

1 Halve the tomatoes and grill until fairly soft.
2 Slice the onion, fry in hot fat till brown and keep hot.
3 Scramble the eggs with the butter, season and pile on the tomatoes.
4 Put some onion rings on top and serve hot.
5 Garnish with parsley.

Spinach ramekins

cooking time   10 minutes

you will need:

4–6 oz. cooked creamed   2 oz. finely grated cheese
  spinach   (including a little
seasoning—including   Parmesan if possible)
  paprika pepper   2 eggs

1 Divide the spinach between 4 small ramekin dishes.
2 Beat the eggs well, adding seasoning and most of the cheese.
3 Pour over the spinach, dusting the top of each ramekin with the last of the cheese.

Put near the top of a hot oven (425–450°F.—Gas Mark 6–7) for 10 minutes until the egg mixture is just set.
Dust with cayenne pepper and serve at once.

Prairie oyster

no cooking

Put into a small cup or glass $\frac{1}{2}$ teaspoon of vinegar and a pinch of salt.
Break into it a very fresh egg and let it be swallowed whole. This is considered one of the lightest ways of serving an egg.

Savoury poached eggs

cooking time   30 minutes

you will need:

2 onions	little cheese
2 tomatoes	cheese sauce (page 44)
4 poached eggs	

1 Boil the chopped onions until tender, drain and season well.
2 Heat for a few minutes with chopped tomatoes.
3 Half fill some fire-proof cases with the mixture of onion and tomato, add a poached egg, cover with some cheese sauce.
4 Finally add some grated cheese and brown under the grill.

Scrambled eggs with Jerusalem artichokes

cooking time   8 minutes

you will need:

1 large or 2 small cooked artichokes	1 teaspoon chopped parsley
4 eggs	1 tablespoon cottage or cream cheese

1 Dice the artichokes and stir into the egg mixture as given in next recipe for tomatoes.
2 Omit the herbs but add the cheese.

Scrambled egg with tomatoes

cooking time   6–8 minutes

you will need:

4 eggs	1 level teaspoon finely chopped parsley or chives
2 tablespoons milk	
1 large tomato	$\frac{1}{2}$ oz. butter
salt and pepper	

1 Whip the eggs and milk.
2 Add the skinned, diced tomato and the parsley or chives, season.

3 Heat butter in a small pan, when hot toss in the further nut of butter, stir and scramble in usual way.

Scotch woodcock

cooking time   8–10 minutes

you will need:

4–6 eggs	little milk
1 oz. butter	8 anchovy fillets
seasoning	4 slices buttered toast
few capers	

1 Heat the butter in a pan, beat the eggs with seasoning and a little milk.
2 Scramble slowly and when set pile on to buttered toast and garnish with the anchovy fillets. A few capers can also be put on top. Toast should be omitted for strict diets.

Stuffed eggs au gratin

cooking time   15 minutes

you will need:

6–8 eggs	chopped parsley
2–3 oz. salami, ham or lean bacon	softened butter
salt and pepper	2 tablespoons finely grated cheese

1 Hard-boil the eggs and cut them in half lengthways.
2 Remove the yolks and mix with the finely chopped salami, ham or bacon, seasonings, parsley and butter.
3 Return the mixture to the whites.
4 Put into a heatproof dish, sprinkle with cheese and brown under a hot grill or in the oven.
5 Serve with crisp salad.

Stuffed hard-boiled eggs

no cooking

Halve two eggs, take out yolks and mash. Fill with any of the following:
Filling 1: 2 oz. cream cheese, little chopped parsley, paprika pepper.
Combine ingredients, return to egg cases, dust tops with paprika and parsley.
Filling 2: 2 oz. chopped ham, little mayonnaise, little gherkin.
Combine ingredients, return to egg cases using gherkin as garnish.
Filling 3: Little curry powder and chutney, knob of butter.
Combine ingredients, return to egg cases.
Serve stuffed eggs on bed of lettuce.

Cheese pudding

cooking time   30 minutes

you will need:

4 oz. grated cheese	1 pint milk
2 eggs	½ teaspoon celery salt
4 starch-reduced rolls	pinch of pepper, nutmeg
1 oz. butter	and mustard

1 Heat the milk and pour over the rolls, which should be broken up.
2 Stir in the butter, seasonings, cheese and well-beaten eggs.
3 Pour into a greased dish and bake in a moderately hot oven (375°F.—Gas Mark 5) for 30 minutes.
4 Serve with creamed vegetables.

Cheese savoury

cooking time   10–15 minutes

1 Break an egg into a lightly greased oven-proof dish, sprinkle with 1 oz. grated Cheddar cheese.
2 Bake in a moderate oven for 10–15 minutes.

Cheese and tomato bakes

cooking time   10 minutes

you will need:

8 good-sized tomatoes	4–6 oz. diced Cheddar
little butter	cheese
	seasoning

1 Cut the tops off the tomatoes and scoop out the centre pulp.
2 Mix this with the diced cheese and pack back tightly into the seasoned tomato cases, put a little butter on top and cover with the lid.
3 Bake for about 10 minutes in a moderately hot oven (400°F.—Gas Mark 5) and serve at once.

Cheese and tomato soufflé

cooking time   30–35 minutes

you will need:

1 oz. margarine	¼ pint tomato juice
½ oz. cornflour	seasoning
2–3 oz. grated cheese	yolks of 3 and whites
mustard	of 4 eggs

1 Heat margarine in a saucepan then stir in the cornflour, away from the heat.
2 Return to the heat again and cook the roux gently for about 3 minutes.
3 Add the tomato juice (again away from the heat), stirring all the time.
4 Cook steadily until a thick sauce, cool slightly, then stir in the beaten egg yolks, cheese and seasoning, including a good pinch mustard.
5 Whisk the egg whites until very stiff then FOLD them gently into the mixture. This isn't difficult to do if you use a palette knife or metal spoon but do not be rough, otherwise you lose the lightness of the eggs.
6 Pour into the dish, about half-filling it. Bake for 25–30 minutes in the centre of a moderately hot oven (400°F.—Gas Mark 5).
7 Bring out of the oven and serve at once.

Cheese custard

1 Serving

cooking time   45 minutes

you will need:

1 egg	good pinch salt, pepper
⅓–½ pint milk	mustard
tomatoes	mushrooms
spinach	little margarine
3 oz. grated cheese	

1 Beat the egg with seasonings, add warm milk, cheese.
2 Pour into pie dish and bake for 45 minutes in centre of very moderate oven (325–350°F.—Gas Mark 3) until custard is set.
3 Stand the pie dish in a large container with cold water in it. This prevents custard curdling.
4 Bake tomatoes and a few mushrooms in a covered dish in the oven, putting a little margarine on the mushrooms.
5 Serve with spinach.

Cheese pie

cooking time   40 minutes

you will need:

4 starch-reduced rolls,	pinch salt and pepper
halved and spread thinly	1 crushed starch-reduced
with butter	roll
6 oz. cheese	1 small onion
2 eggs	1 pint milk

1 Line a buttered pie dish with the rolls.
2 Beat the eggs with the seasonings, stir in the grated onion, 5 oz. grated cheese and the milk.
3 Pour into the lined dish and stand 30 minutes.
4 Grate the rest of the cheese, mix with the crumbs and sprinkle on.
5 Bake in a very moderate oven (350°F.—Gas Mark 3) for 40 minutes.
6 Serve hot with onion sauce (page 44) and vegetables.

Danish blue cheese mousse

cooking time   few minutes to melt jelly

you will need:

1 packet lemon jelly	1 tablespoon
4 oz. Danish blue cheese	Worcestershire sauce
2 heaped tablespoons	2 stalks celery
mayonnaise	2 eating apples
1 small red pepper	$\frac{1}{4}$ pint evaporated milk
$\frac{1}{2}$ pint water	or cream
	1 tablespoon lemon juice

Make up the jelly with water and leave until nearly setting.

Crumble the cheese and mash down with a fork, add the mayonnaise, diced pepper, celery and apple.

Whip the evaporated milk with lemon juice and fold into the cheese mixture, then fold in the jelly and Worcestershire sauce.

Mix well and pour into a mould and leave to set.

When firm, turn out and serve.

Iced Camembert cheese

no cooking

Iced Camembert cheese is a delicious savoury at the end of a meal, particularly in hot weather.

Remove rind from the cheese if wished, mix with a little cream and put into the freezing tray and leave until lightly frozen.

Serve with starch-reduced rolls.

Low calorie macaroni cheese

cooking time   12–25 minutes

you will need:

4 oz. macaroni	2 oz. grated Parmesan
$\frac{1}{4}$ pint milk	cheese
4 oz. grated Cheddar	1 oz. grated cheese for
cheese	topping

Put the macaroni into about $1\frac{1}{2}$ pints boiling water, to which you have added a level teaspoon salt.

2 Cook steadily until the macaroni is just tender. Do no overcook; elbow length quick cooking macaroni takes only 7 minutes.

3 Drain in a colander, mix with milk, cheese and heat gently.

4 Sprinkle cheese on top.

5 To get rid of some of the starchiness of macaroni it can be rinsed under hot tap before mixing with milk and cheese.

6 If you like a more moist macaroni cheese then use $\frac{3}{4}$ pint cheese sauce to the same

quantity of cooked macaroni, but this is considerably higher in calories.

Low calorie cheese soufflé

cooking time   30 minutes

you will need:

3 eggs	2 tablespoons milk
8 oz. cottage cheese	seasoning
1 oz. margarine or butter	mustard

1 Melt butter in a saucepan, heat gently for a minute or so, draw pan to one side and gradually add milk.

2 Add cheese to contents of pan and beat until smooth.

3 Carefully separate the yolks from the whites of the eggs, season yolks with salt and pepper and pinch mustard.

4 Lightly beat the egg yolks and add them to the cheese and milk mixture. It is essential to stir them in well.

5 Whisk the egg whites until very stiff (you should be able to turn the basin upside down without the whites falling out). Lightly fold the mixture into these with a spatula.

6 Pour the mixture into a buttered dish (with greaseproof paper reaching 2 inches above side). Bake for about 25 minutes in centre of moderately hot oven (400°F.—Gas Mark 5).

Variations:
Fish soufflé

As above but use about 4 oz. flaked cooked fish instead of cheese.

Ham soufflé

As above but use about 4 oz. minced or finely chopped cooked ham instead of cheese.

Mushroom soufflé

As above but fry gently about 4 oz. mushrooms, chop finely and add to mixture in place of cheese. Use milk in place of tomato juice.

Spinach soufflé

As above but stir about 4 oz. cooked sieved spinach into milk mixture instead of cheese. Or you can use both spinach and cheese. Use milk instead of tomato juice.

Savoury custard

cooking time   25 minutes

you will need:

2 eggs	few mixed cooked
2 oz. grated cheese	vegetables (peas, onions,
⅓ pint milk	beans, cauliflower)
	seasoning

1 Beat the eggs and add the milk.
2 Season this custard well.
3 Arrange the vegetables in the pie dish and pour the custard carefully over them.
4 Sprinkle the cheese on top.
5 Bake in the middle of a moderate oven (375°F.—Gas Mark 4) for approximately 25 minutes until the custard has set.

Savoury kidneys

cooking time   15 minutes

you will need:

2 onions	¼ pint brown stock (or
1 oz. margarine or fat	water with a little beef
2 tomatoes	or yeast extract)
2 rashers bacon	seasoning
4 lambs' kidneys	parsley

1 Slice the onions very thinly. Fry in the hot margarine together with the diced bacon (care should be taken NOT to brown the onions).
2 Add skinned chopped tomatoes.
3 Remove fat from kidneys and cut into neat pieces or halves.
4 Add the diced kidneys to the onions and cook for several minutes, gradually add the stock.
5 Bring to the boil, stirring well and cook until kidneys are tender.
6 Season. Garnish with parsley.

Kidneys and scrambled egg

cooking time   10–15 minutes

you will need:

2 lambs' kidneys	squeeze lemon juice
4 eggs	4 slices fried bread or
1 oz. butter	buttered toast
seasoning	

1 Cut the kidneys into small pieces, season well.
2 Heat butter and cook kidneys in this for about 7–8 minutes, if necessary add 1 tablespoon water to prevent sticking.
3 Add lemon juice.
4 Beat and season eggs lightly, add to kidney and continue cooking.
Toast or fried bread should be omitted for strict diets.

Smoked haddock

cooking time   5 minutes

you will need:

smoked haddock	margarine
poached egg	water

1 Cook haddock steadily for about 5 minutes, covering pan.
2 Put a tiny knob of margarine on top before serving.
3 Top with poached egg.

Haddock and egg scramble

cooking time   5–8 minutes

you will need:

4–6 oz. cooked smoked	4 eggs
haddock	seasoning

1 Flake the fish, add to the beaten eggs with pepper and little, if any, salt.
2 Heat a knob of margarine in a saucepan and cook gently, stirring well.

Smoked haddock with tomatoes

cooking time   10 minutes

you will need:

4 oz. cooked smoked	1 teaspoon chopped onion
haddock	1 dessertspoon cream
½ oz. butter	seasoning
1 tomato	

1 Shred fish from skin and bone.
2 Melt the butter in a small saucepan and put in the onion, very finely chopped.
3 Cook it a minute or two then add the tomato peeled and sliced, fish and seasoning.
4 Stir over the heat for a few minutes longer and add the cream just before serving.

Herring roes

cooking time   10–15 minutes

Herring roes are an excellent dish for breakfast or supper. Cook in one of the following ways.

1 After washing, put on to a plate with a small knob of margarine, a little milk and seasoning. Cover with a second plate and steam for about 15 minutes over a pan of boiling water. This keeps the roes moist and whole but is rather slow for breakfast.
2 Wash and dry the roes. Heat about 1 oz. margarine in a pan and cook until golden coloured.
3 Cook in a saucepan in a little milk, until just soft. Season well.

Ham and asparagus rolls

Spread some thinly cut lean ham with French mustard and put a piece of butter lightly on top.
Put a cooked or canned asparagus head at one end and roll up tightly.

Asparagus cheese layer pie

cooking time   40–45 minutes

you will need:

4 oz. quick cooking macaroni	1 14 oz. can asparagus (drained)
4 oz. grated cheese	8 oz. tomatoes

Cook macaroni. Drain.
Place alternate layers of asparagus, macaroni, tomatoes and cheese in greased 2-pint pie dish, finishing with a layer of cheese.
Bake in moderately hot oven (400°F.—Gas Mark 5) for 20–25 minutes.

Asparagus with egg sauce

cooking time   25 minutes

you will need:

½ pint egg sauce (page 43)	2 hard-boiled eggs asparagus

1 Cook prepared asparagus until tender in a pan of boiling salted water.
2 Arrange the asparagus in a dish, pour egg sauce over.
3 Arrange hard-boiled eggs over the sauce to garnish.

Stuffed aubergines no. 1

2 Servings

cooking time   30 minutes

you will need:

2 medium sized aubergines	1 tablespoon chopped parsley
½ teaspoon salt	salt and pepper
2 teaspoons olive oil or butter	3 oz. grated Cheddar cheese
2 oz. diced cooked lean meat	½ tablespoon finely chopped cooked onion
1 skinned chopped tomato	

1 Wash aubergines, remove stalk and cut in half lengthwise.
2 Cut round each half aubergine ¼-inch from the skin and then score the surface lightly to ensure even cooking.
3 Sprinkle with salt and brush with olive oil or melted butter.
4 Put on a greased baking tin in a moderately hot oven (400°F.—Gas Mark 5) until the centre is nearly cooked, 15–20 minutes.

5 Make stuffing by mixing all the ingredients together except a little cheese.
6 Scoop out about half the flesh from the centre of aubergines, chop up and add to stuffing.
6 Fill aubergine cases with stuffing, sprinkle with rest of grated cheese and return to the oven for 15 minutes.

Stuffed aubergines no. 2

cooking time   1 hour

you will need:

8 oz. onions	2 apples
1 oz. fat	seasoning
1 lb. tomatoes	3 or 4 aubergines

1 Fry the chopped onions in the fat and add the quartered tomatoes and diced apples.
2 Cook slowly until tender, and add seasoning.
3 Blanch the aubergines in boiling water for 8–10 minutes, then split lengthwise.
4 Remove the pulp, mix with the tomato and onion mixture and refill the cases.
5 Place in a greased fireproof dish and cook in a slow oven for 1 hour (275–300°F.—Gas Mark 1–2).

Aubergine provençale

cooking time   15 minutes

you will need:

1 aubergine	parsley
1 shallot or onion	4 large tomatoes
1 oz. butter or 1 tablespoon oil	clove of garlic
	seasoning

1 Wash aubergine and cut into thin slices, removing any seeds. Peel if wished.
2 Heat the butter or oil and fry the finely chopped shallot and crushed clove of garlic, then fry the aubergine until tender.
3 Meanwhile skin and quarter the tomatoes.
4 Toss tomatoes and aubergine together until tomatoes are softened and garnish with chopped parsley.

Baked bean casserole

2 Servings

cooking time   30 minutes

you will need:

small can baked beans	1 green pepper
3 tomatoes	2 rashers bacon
1 onion	

1 Mix beans with sliced tomatoes, finely sliced onion, chopped green pepper and lean rashers of bacon.
2 Put in covered dish and cook gently for 30 minutes.

Broccoli, mushroom and tomato pie

cooking time	25 minutes

you will need:

1 lb. broccoli	½ pint cheese sauce
4 oz. mushrooms	(page 44)
2 tomatoes	1 oz. butter

1 Prepare and boil the broccoli for 20 minutes or till tender, drain, divide into flowerets and finely slice stems.
2 Meanwhile, brown the sliced mushrooms in butter.
3 Peel and dice the tomatoes.
4 Turn the cooked broccoli, mushrooms and tomatoes into a buttered pie dish, pour in the sauce. Serve hot.

Cabbage rolls

3 Servings

cooking time	50–60 minutes

you will need:

5–6 large cabbage leaves	1 dessertspoon
8 oz. minced lean beef	Worcestershire sauce
(uncooked if possible)	little milk if necessary
1 small onion	little stock or tomato
1 egg	juice
	seasoning to taste

1 Wash the cabbage leaves and drain.
2 Mix together all the other ingredients, except the tomato juice.
3 Place this filling on the cabbage leaves and roll up.
4 Arrange in a greased oven-proof dish and pour on a little stock or tomato juice.
5 Cover dish and bake in centre of a very moderate oven (350°F.—Gas Mark 3) for 50–60 minutes until tender.
6 Drain and serve with stock or tomato juice.

Cabbage with mustard dressing

cooking time	7–10 minutes

you will need:

1 medium sized cabbage	vinegar
1 oz. butter	2 teaspoons mustard
rings of tomato	made with vinegar

1 Cut the cabbage in strips and cook it in as little salted water as possible without letting it burn.
2 Combine made mustard with melted butter.
3 Drain cabbage well and then, while it is still hot, toss it with two forks in the dressing.
4 If you mix the cabbage and dressing quickly, it should keep hot enough for serving straight away.
5 Heap up the cabbage and garnish with rings of tomato.

Spiced red cabbage

cooking time	40 minutes

you will need:

1 small red cabbage	2 sweet apples
a little butter	little chopped onion
¼ pint water	1 tablespoon lemon juice
salt	

1 Shred the cabbage very finely.
2 Put the butter and a little water in a saucepan.
2 Add the cabbage, chopped onion, salt to taste and the peeled, cored, sliced apples.
4 Cover the saucepan closely and simmer for 45 minutes.
5 Add a little more butter and lemon juice and simmer for another 5 minutes before serving.

Cauliflower and cheese Charlotte

cooking time	25–30 minutes

you will need:

1 cauliflower	4 oz. grated cheese
seasoning	2–3 tablespoons milk
½ oz. butter	few slices tomato
parsley to garnish	

1 Cook cauliflower in boiling salted water until tender.
2 Drain well and beat until soft purée.
3 Put half in dish, cover with half the cheese and seasoning.
4 Add rest of cauliflower, cheese, butter, seasoning, milk and place tomato slices on top.
5 Bake for 10 or 15 minutes near top of fairly hot oven (425°F.—Gas Mark 6).
6 Garnish with parsley.

Cauliflower Palermo

cooking time	25 minutes

you will need:

1 large cauliflower	1 oz. cornflour
1 small can shrimps or	2 oz. grated cheese
4 oz. fresh or frozen	1 teaspoon
shrimps or prawns	Worcestershire sauce
¾ pint tomato juice	pepper and salt
1 oz. butter	lemon juice

1 Cook the cauliflower carefully to retain its shape.
2 Drain and place on a large serving dish and keep hot.
3 Make a sauce with the butter, cornflour and tomato juice. Add the lemon juice, Worcestershire sauce and seasonings to taste.
4 Stir in half cheese and the drained shrimps.
5 Pour over the cauliflower and sprinkle with the remaining cheese.
6 Brown under the grill.

Golden cauliflower

cooking time 20 minutes

you will need:

1 cauliflower	$\frac{1}{2}$ oz. butter
1 tablespoon chopped parsley	1 chopped hard-boiled egg

1 Sprig cauliflower and boil in salted water until just tender.
2 Drain when cooked and put in hot dish.
3 Heat butter with egg and parsley.
4 Sprinkle over cauliflower.

Cauliflower and bacon savoury

cooking time 15 minutes

you will need:

1 large cauliflower	2 oz. grated cheese
1 onion	seasoning
4 rashers bacon	pinch of cayenne pepper

1 Trim the cauliflower, cutting it into medium sized sprigs.
2 Wash well. Cook in about $\frac{1}{2}$ pint salted water until just tender (8–10 minutes). Drain.
3 Arrange the cauliflower in a greased pie dish or entrée dish.
4 Skin and chop the onion, trim and chop the bacon.
5 Fry these together lightly until the onion looks transparent but is not browned. Sprinkle over the cauliflower, with the cheese, and brown under the grill.

Cauliflower with mushrooms and eggs

cooking time 20 minutes

you will need:

1 cooked cauliflower	$\frac{1}{2}$ pint cheese sauce (page 44)
4 oz. mushrooms	
2 hard-boiled eggs	grated cheese
butter	

1 Stew mushrooms.
2 Put the sprigs of cooked cauliflower in a buttered fireproof dish, cover with mushrooms, sliced eggs and pour the cheese sauce over. Sprinkle on grated cheese.
3 Reheat under the grill.

Cauliflower with cottage cheese

no cooking

you will need:

1 cooked cauliflower	French dressing (page 45)
4 oz. cottage cheese	
3 olives	pinch of paprika
	milk

1 Arrange the flowerets of cold cooked cauliflower on a dish.

2 Sprinkle French dressing over.
3 Cream the cheese with very little top milk and a dessertspoon of dressing and pipe it around the cauliflower, then sprinkle very little paprika on it, here and there.
4 Garnish with sliced olives. Serve cold.

Cauliflower poached eggs

cooking time 30 minutes

you will need:

4 poached eggs	2 oz. cheese
1 cauliflower	pinch of red pepper
1 oz. margarine	salt

1 Cook the cauliflower until soft, add seasoning and margarine.
2 Arrange in casserole with cheese and brown under grill.
3 Top with a poached egg per person and serve on toast with the eggs, sprinkled with pepper.

Celeriac with egg and cheese sauce

cooking time 25 minutes

you will need:

2 roots celeriac or celery	$\frac{1}{2}$ pint egg sauce (page 43)
2 hard-boiled eggs	

1 Peel and scrub some small roots of celeriac or celery and cut into neat slices $\frac{1}{4}$-inch thick.
2 Simmer for 30 minutes or till tender.
3 Use cooking liquid with milk to make sauce.
4 Put the cooked celeriac in a buttered baking dish, pour the sauce over.
5 Garnish with hard-boiled eggs.

Celery italienne

cooking time 30 minutes

you will need:

4 small or 2 large heads of celery	2 onions
4 rashers of bacon	2 oz. margarine
seasoning	8 oz. tomatoes or can tomatoes
2 tablespoons celery stock	2 oz. mushrooms

1 Trim celery heads so they are the same size. If using large heads divide each one into halves. Use any 'odd' pieces of celery for flavouring stews or sauces.
2 Cook in boiling salted water until just tender.
3 Meanwhile heat margarine and fry the chopped onion and mushrooms until tender.
4 Add the tomatoes (which should be skinned), and when quite soft add celery stock. Bring to the boil, season well, adding lemon juice.
5 Grill 4 rashers of bacon then roll round each head of cooked celery and serve with sauce.

Corn bake

cooking time   35–45 minutes

you will need:

1 can corn on cob or frozen corn	1 oz. butter
milk	1 tablespoon flour
	2 eggs separated

1 Cook corn until tender or drain can, reserving liquid.
2 Make the liquid up to $\frac{1}{2}$ pint with milk.
3 Melt the butter, add the flour and make a sauce with the liquid stirring well all the time.
4 Add the corn and stir until the mixture boils.
5 Cool slightly and stir in well beaten egg yolks.
6 Season and cook until mixture thickens slightly. Cool.
7 Fold in the stiffly beaten egg whites. Pour into dish.
8 Bake in a moderate oven (375°F.—Gas Mark 4) for 30 minutes.

Corn toasties

cooking time   10–25 minutes

you will need:

1 can corn or 2 corn cobs	1 oz. butter
2 tomatoes	$\frac{1}{2}$ onion
2 oz. ham	1 oz. grated cheese
2 oz. mushrooms (optional)	

1 Cook corn cobs and strip off cobs.
2 Heat butter in pan and gently sauté finely chopped onion, chopped tomatoes and mushrooms.
3 Drain corn and add to mixture in pan.
4 Heat gently and stir in chopped ham.
5 Serve in individual dishes or on slices of toast, sprinkled with grated cheese and grilled until golden brown.

Cheese and cucumber soufflé

4–6 Servings

cooking time   few minutes

you will need:

$\frac{1}{2}$ pint aspic jelly*	salt and pepper
1 tablespoon tarragon vinegar	$\frac{1}{2}$ teaspoon mustard
6 oz. grated Cheddar cheese	pinch onion salt
	2 eggs
$\frac{1}{2}$ cucumber (peeled and diced)	**To decorate:**
	cucumber slices

*Use a little more of the aspic jelly to the $\frac{1}{2}$ pint water than usual, or dissolve $\frac{1}{4}$ level teaspoon powder gelatine WITH the aspic jelly.

1 Beat egg yolks until thick.
2 Make up aspic jelly in small basin, stir in vinegar and allow to cool, but not set. Add to egg yolks.
3 Mix cheese, seasoning, mustard and onion salt.
4 When aspic jelly mixture is starting to thicken stir in cucumber then cheese mixture.
5 Whip egg whites, fold into cheese mixture and pour mixture into 1-pint soufflé dish with band of greaseproof paper round outside.
6 Chill until set.
7 Remove band of paper and garnish with cucumber slices.

Cucumber eggs

cooking time   15–20 minutes

you will need:

6 sliced half-cooked eggs	4 small onions thinly shredded
1 oz. margarine	$\frac{1}{2}$ tablespoon vinegar
3 small cucumbers or 1 large cucumber	pepper and salt
1 tablespoon cream or milk	

1 Dissolve the margarine in a saucepan.
2 Peel, quarter and cut the cucumbers, shred the onions and add these to the margarine, flavouring with pepper and salt and finally adding vinegar.
3 Simmer the mixture for 10 minutes, stirring well, add the eggs sliced.
4 Warm for 2 minutes and stir in the cream.

Chopped cucumber and yoghourt

no cooking

1 Peel and roughly chop 2–3 inches of a fresh crisp cucumber.
2 Sprinkle with freshly ground black pepper.
3 Mix with a bottle of well-chilled yoghourt and heap up in pastry shells. (If on a strict diet you omit the pastry.)
4 You can make this salad in pastry into a meal, by serving with it a good portion of cottage cheese, blended with a little top of the milk and flavoured with chopped chives or the chopped green tops of spring onions.

Cooked cucumber

cooking time   10 minutes

1 First peel cucumber. Cut in 1–$1\frac{1}{2}$ inch slices.
2 Put into small quantity of boiling salted water and cook until tender (about 10 minutes).
3 Drain and serve with a very little hot butter.
4 Garnish with chopped parsley or chives and paprika pepper.

Stuffed cucumber with mushrooms and beef

cooking time   50 minutes

you will need:

1 large cucumber
4 oz. chopped mushrooms
8 oz. minced beef (lean)
seasoning
½ oz. margarine or dripping
little tomato purée or
  juice

1 Skin the cucumber and cut into 3-inch lengths, then cut lengthways through each piece.
2 Take out the centre and chop this finely.
3 Heat the margarine in a saucepan and toss in the chopped mushrooms for a few minutes.
4 Stir in the meat and season well.
5 Put the pieces of cucumber into boiling salted water and cook for 5 minutes only.
6 Drain carefully and fill with the meat mixture.
7 Put the stuffed cucumber in a dish covered with tomato juice or purée and bake in the middle of a moderate oven (375°F.—Gas Mark 4) for 35–40 minutes.
8 Serve with spinach and the tomato juice.

Hot slaw

cooking time   4–5 minutes

you will need:

¼ pint single cream or
  yoghourt
grated raw white cabbage
salt and pepper
1 tablespoon wine
  vinegar

1 Place the cabbage in a thick pan with the cream, salt and pepper to season and the wine vinegar.
2 Cook over a low heat, stirring constantly for 4–5 minutes and serve at once.

Leeks au gratin

cooking time   20 minutes

you will need:

1½ lb. leeks
little grated cheese
cheese sauce (page 44)

1 Wash leeks and cut into even lengths, boil till tender.
2 Arrange in a greased fireproof dish, pour the sauce over the leeks.
3 Sprinkle grated cheese over the sauce and brown under the grill.

Marrow and mushroom au gratin

cooking time   50 minutes

you will need:

1 small vegetable marrow
4 oz. mushrooms
1 heart celery
1 onion
4 oz. cheese
1 egg
butter
seasoning

1 Slice the mushrooms, celery and onion.
2 Stew with a little water. Season well.
3 Boil the marrow, whole, for 20 minutes, cool, peel, cut into rings.
4 Beat the egg and mix with the drained celery, mushrooms and onion.
5 Put half the marrow rings in a buttered pie dish, spread the vegetable batter over, cover with 3 oz. thinly sliced cheese and rest of the marrow.
6 Grate remaining cheese, sprinkle over, dot with butter.
7 Bake for 30 minutes in a moderate oven (375°F.—Gas Mark 4).

Stuffed marrow no. 1

cooking time   1 hour 10 minutes

you will need:

medium sized marrow
2 onions
4 oz. mushrooms
8 oz. cooked meat
2 tomatoes
1 oz. dripping
salt and pepper
1 teaspoon chopped
  parsley
a pinch of thyme

1 Wash the marrow and halve.
2 Scoop out the seeds.
3 Peel and chop the onions, tomatoes and mushrooms and chop or mince the cold meat.
4 Fry the onions then add the mushrooms, tomatoes, seasonings and herbs and cook for a few minutes.
5 Now add the meat and reheat quickly.
6 Fill each marrow half with this stuffing, cover with greased paper and cook in a moderate oven (375°F.—Gas Mark 4) for 1 hour.

Stuffed marrow no. 2

cooking time   1½ hours

you will need:

1 medium marrow
8 oz. calves' liver
2 oz. ham
baked tomatoes
seasoning
1 onion
½ teaspoon mixed herbs
1 egg

1 Peel the marrow and remove a slice from the top.
2 Scrape out the seeds and make a hole for the filling.
3 Chop the liver, ham and onion very finely and mix with the herbs, seasoning and egg.
4 Stuff the marrow and replace the slice, wrap carefully in greaseproof paper and steam for 1½ hours.
5 Serve sliced with baked tomatoes.

Ham and mushroom custard

cooking time   1 hour

you will need:

2 eggs	2 oz. chopped cooked
seasoning	ham
¾ pint milk	2 oz. chopped cooked
	mushrooms

1 Lightly beat the eggs, season and add the milk, ham and mushrooms.
2 Pour the mixture into a fireproof dish and cook in a very slow oven (275°F.—Gas Mark 1) until set—about 1 hour.

Sautéed mushrooms with eggs

cooking time   10 minutes

you will need:

1 oz. butter	salt and pepper
12 oz. small mushrooms	2–3 hard-boiled eggs
2 tablespoons milk	tomatoes

1 Heat the butter and sauté the prepared and seasoned mushrooms for 5 minutes, turning them frequently.
2 Add the milk and simmer for further 5 minutes.
3 Chop the eggs coarsely and add to the mushrooms.
4 Serve in border of grilled tomatoes.

Stuffed mushrooms

4–5 Servings as Hors-d'oeuvre
1 Serving as Main Dish

cooking time   25 minutes

you will need:

4 or 5 medium sized	1 teaspoon finely chopped
mushrooms	parsley
1 tablespoon cooked ham	1 tablespoon fine starch-
1 teaspoon finely chopped	reduced breadcrumbs
onion	1 tablespoon cream
½ oz. butter or margarine	or top of the milk
seasoning	1 large tomato
	parsley to garnish

1 Peel the mushrooms, remove the stalks and wash, if necessary.
2 Chop the ham and mushroom stalks.
3 Melt the fat in a saucepan and fry the onion slightly.
4 Add all the other ingredients except the tomato and mushroom tops.
5 Pile the filling on each mushroom.
6 Place them on a greased tin, cover with a greased paper and bake in a moderate oven until tender—about 20 minutes.
7 Place a thin slice of tomato on each dish, stand a mushroom on each and garnish with parsley.

Mushroom casserole

cooking time   35 minutes

you will need:

12 oz. mushrooms	2 sticks of celery or use
3 tomatoes	cooked beans
1 onion	1 tablespoon chopped
1 oz. butter	parsley
seasoning	4 tablespoons stock or
	water

1 Grease a casserole.
2 Peel and stalk the mushrooms, skin the tomatoes, cut the onion in rings and toss in the butter. Use both heads and stalks of mushrooms.
3 Fill the dish with alternate layers of chopped celery and the other ingredients, seasoning each layer well, sprinkle with a little parsley and finish with a layer of mushrooms on top.
4 Add the liquid and stew gently in a moderate oven until tender (375°F.—Gas Mark 4) about 30 minutes.

Mushroom and parsley stuffing

cooking time   10 minutes

you will need:

4 oz. mushrooms	1 chopped shallot or
4 oz. parsley	onion
½ oz. butter	seasoning

1 Chop shallot or onion, fry gently in the butter for 5 minutes.
2 Add the finely chopped mushrooms and fry 5 minutes more.
3 Add parsley.
Use for stuffing fish and meat.

Mushrooms in white wine

4–6 Servings

cooking time   3 minutes

you will need:

1 lb. small mushrooms	2 lemons
1 tablespoon chopped onion	6 tablespoons white wine
chopped parsley	salt
2 tablespoons olive oil	pepper

1 Choose small mushrooms, wash them thoroughly and dry them.
2 Place the mushrooms in a pan, in which you have already heated the olive oil.
3 Add salt, pepper, onion, the finely chopped parsley, juice of lemons and the white wine.
4 Cover and cook over a fast heat for 3 minutes.
5 Leave to cool.
6 Serve the mushrooms in their juice.
7 If you wish, a little mustard can be added to the juice.

Mushroom eggs

cooking time   10–15 minutes

you will need:

4 oz. mushrooms   4 tablespoons milk
a little butter   seasoning
4 eggs

1 Chop the mushrooms and fry lightly in the butter.
2 Put a little of the mixture in the bottom of 4 ramekin dishes, then add an egg and lastly 1 tablespoon milk and seasoning to each.
3 Place the dishes in a saucepan containing some boiling water, cover and simmer gently for 10–15 minutes, until the eggs are set.
4 Serve at once.

Devilled mushrooms and eggs

cooking time   10–15 minutes

you will need:

2 oz. mushrooms   1 teaspoon Worcester-
3 hard-boiled eggs   shire sauce
1 oz. butter   1 teaspoon mustard
good pinch curry powder   ketchup
½–1 teaspoon made
    mustard

1 Heat butter, fry chopped mushrooms in it, add flavourings.
2 When mushrooms are cooked add quartered hard-boiled eggs.
3 Heat and serve at once.

Baked onions

cooking time   1½ hours

1 To bake onions keep on the skins and put into a dish with a little milk and seasoning and cook in the centre of a moderate oven (375°F.—Gas Mark 4) until tender.
2 This will take approximately 1½ hours for medium sized onions.
3 Buttered paper can be put over if desired.
4 Remove skin just before serving.

Casseroled onions

cooking time   1–2 hours

you will need:

8 small or 4 good-sized   ½ pint brown stock or
   onions   tomato juice
seasoning   2 oz. fat
                  1 oz. flour

1 Put the onions with the liquid in a casserole, covered tightly and bake for 1–2 hours in a very moderate oven (375°F.—Gas Mark 3).
2 Some of the liquid can be served with them.

Stuffed onions

cooking time   1½ hours

you will need:

onions   celery
cheese   red or green pepper

1 Allow 1 large onion per person.
2 Cook for about 25 minutes in boiling salted water, then remove from the liquid, take out centre of onion and chop finely.
3 Mix this with little chopped celery, grated cheese, seasoning and little chopped pepper if available (green or red can be used).
4 Pile into centre of onion.
5 Bake in covered dish for about 1 hour in very moderate oven (350°F.—Gas Mark 3).
6 Serve with watercress.

Onion savoury

cooking time   approximately 2 hours

you will need:

1 lb. button onions   2 bay leaves
1 oz. butter   6 peppercorns
4 oz. cheese   1 clove garlic
2 tomatoes

1 Cook onions, chopped garlic, butter, bay leaves and peppercorns in a covered casserole in slow oven (275–300°F.—Gas Mark 1–2) for 2 hours.
2 Lift lid, cover with very thinly sliced cheese and slice the tomatoes over.
3 Place in a hot oven for 5 minutes or under the grill till the cheese melts.
Excellent with eggs.

Jamaican peppers

no cooking

you will need:

1 can corn or 2 cooked   4 red or green sweet
   corn cobs   peppers
12 prawns, coarsely   1 medium sized onion,
   chopped   chopped
prawns for decoration   chopped parsley
                  salad dressing (page 44)

1 Strip corn off cob.
2 Cut a third off the peppers lengthwise and remove core and seeds. Blanch for 5 minutes in boiling salted water and cool.
3 Finely chop remaining third of peppers, and mix with chopped onion, parsley, prawns and corn.
4 Toss this mixture in well seasoned salad dressing.
5 Fill peppers with mixture, arrange on bed of lettuce leaves and decorate with whole prawns.

Green peppers with cream cheese

no cooking

you will need:

tomatoes	sliced tomatoes
cream or curd cheese	peppers
salad dressing (page 44)	

1 Cut out the stem end of the peppers, remove pips, stuff with cream cheese or curd cheese blended with salad dressing.
2 Chill well, cut into slices.
3 Dish up with a garnish of sliced tomatoes.

Stuffed peppers

cooking time   25 minutes

you will need:

2 large or 4 small red or green peppers	6 oz. chopped lean ham
	2 large tomatoes
1 teaspoon mixed herbs	seasoning

1 Slice the peppers in half lengthways and remove the seeds.
2 Parboil in salted water for a few minutes.
3 Mix the chopped ham, chopped tomatoes, seasoning and mixed herbs together and fill the halves of pepper.
4 Place in an ovenware dish and bake in a moderately hot oven (400°F.—Gas Mark 5) for about 15–20 minutes.

Spinach soufflé

cooking time   25 minutes

you will need:

12 oz. cooked spinach	2 oz. grated Parmesan
2 tablespoons milk	cheese (if desired can
seasoning	be omitted)
4 eggs	

1 Chop finely the spinach, or sieve.
2 Add milk and seasoning.
3 Beat in egg yolks and cheese and stiffly beaten egg whites.
4 Pour into soufflé dish and bake for approximately 25 minutes in centre of moderate oven (375°F.—Gas Mark 4).

Stuffed marrow and spinach

cooking time   40 minutes

you will need:

1 small marrow	1 oz. grated Parmesan
1 lb. spinach	cheese
salt and pepper	1 tablespoon finely
nutmeg	chopped parsley
1 oz. butter	oil

1 Take a small marrow, cut the lid off lengthwise. Scoop out pith and pips and steam for 20 minutes until nearly soft.

2 Cook the spinach, sieve, season with salt, pepper and nutmeg.
3 Add the butter, Parmesan cheese, parsley.
4 Fill the marrow with the stuffing while both are still hot and put into a moderate oven (375°F.—Gas Mark 4) for 20 minutes.

Creamed spinach

cooking time   15–20 minutes

1 Cook spinach until tender, strain and sieve or chop finely with a knife.
2 Return to pan with small knob of butter and a very little cream and heat together.
3 Season well.

Spinach timbales

cooking time   45 minutes

you will need:

8 oz. finely chopped cooked spinach	1 tablespoon butter, melted
$\frac{1}{2}$ teaspoon salt	$\frac{1}{4}$ pint milk
1 teaspoon chopped onion	tomato sauce (page 44)
2 eggs, well beaten	parsley

1 Combine spinach, seasonings, butter, eggs and milk.
2 Turn into 4 greased small moulds, put in pan of hot water and bake in a moderate oven (350°F.—Gas Mark 3) for 45 minutes.
3 Unmould, serve at once with tomato sauce and garnish with parsley.

Tomato and mushroom cups

2 Servings

cooking time   10–15 minutes

you will need:

2 large tomatoes	seasoning
Worcestershire sauce	$\frac{1}{2}$ oz. margarine
3 mushrooms	

1 Remove centres from tomatoes, chop these and mix with chopped uncooked mushrooms.
2 Add seasoning, few drops Worcestershire sauce and a tiny knob of margarine.
3 Pack into tomato cases and bake for 10 minutes in hot oven (450°F.—Gas Mark 7).
4 Serve with hot or cold meat.

Tomato soufflé

cooking time   25 minutes

you will need:

$\frac{1}{2}$ pint thick tomato purée	2 oz. grated Parmesan
3 eggs	cheese
seasoning	2 tablespoons white sauce

1 Separate the egg yolks and whites.
2 Mix all ingredients together with the exception

of egg whites. Beat these to a stiff froth then add to the mixture.

3 Put in a buttered soufflé dish and bake for 25–30 minutes in centre of moderately hot oven (400°F.—Gas Mark 5).

4 Serve immediately.

Tomatoes stuffed with mushrooms

cooking time   15–20 minutes

you will need:

4 large tomatoes	2 eggs
4 mushrooms	seasoning
parsley	1½ oz. butter

1 Chop the mushrooms into small pieces and cook gently in the hot butter.

2 Cut the tops off the tomatoes, scoop out the centre pulp and season the cases.

3 Add the tomato pulp to the mushrooms and the beaten eggs, season well and cook gently until just beginning to stiffen.

4 Put into the tomato cases and bake for 10 minutes in a hot oven (425°F.—Gas Mark 6).

5 Garnish with parsley.

6 Serve with fried bread or crisp toast.

Tomato cups

cooking time   10 minutes

you will need:

4 large tomatoes	2 tablespoons starch-
2 eggs	reduced breadcrumbs
2 oz. grated cheese	seasoning

1 Try and select tomatoes that will stand upright. Cut a slice from the top of each and scoop out the centre pulp. Cut this finely.

2 Whisk the egg yolks, add the tomato pulp, cheese and breadcrumbs and season well.

3 Pile the filling into the tomato cases.

4 Whip the egg whites until very stiff, adding a pinch of salt and pepper. Pile on top of the tomato cases.

5 Put into the centre of a moderate oven (375°F.—Gas Mark 4) for a good 10 minutes.

Tomato meringue

cooking time   10 minutes

you will need:

4 really large firm	2 oz. finely grated
tomatoes	Gruyère or Cheddar
seasoning	cheese
2 egg whites	1 tablespoon diced
paprika pepper	cucumber or gherkins

1 Halve the tomatoes.

2 Scoop out centre pulp.

3 Chop and season well and add nearly all the cheese, the cucumber and seasoning.

4 Pile back into the tomato cases.

5 Whisk egg whites and pile on top of tomatoes.

6 Dust with paprika pepper or, if liked, the last of the grated cheese.

7 Set for 5–10 minutes in a moderate oven.

8 Garnish with peas and serve with creamed spinach.

Tomato and carrot casserole

cooking time   1 hour

you will need:

8 oz. tomatoes	6 oz. minced cooked
1 lb. carrots sliced to	ham or corned beef
about ¼ inch thick	2 chopped onions
1 teaspoon salt	2 cloves
1 oz. butter	2 tablespoons water
½ teaspoon pepper	

1 Melt butter and slowly sauté onions for about 5 minutes.

2 Stir in the remaining ingredients putting water and minced ham in last.

3 Bring to boiling point, then put into a casserole, cover and bake for 1 hour (350°F.—Gas Mark 3).

Tomato and marrow casserole

cooking time   45–50 minutes

you will need:

4 rashers of streaky bacon	1 onion
2 oz. margarine or butter	6 tomatoes
or bacon fat	seasoning
small marrow	

1 Slice the onion and fry in the hot margarine or butter.

2 Add the skinned sliced tomatoes and heat until soft.

3 If the marrow is very young it needs no cooking at all, but if not then dice and steam for 5 minutes only.

4 Chop the bacon into small pieces.

5 Fill a pie dish with the marrow and bacon and top with the tomato and onion mixture. Season.

6 Cover and bake for approximately 35–45 minutes in a moderately hot oven (425°F.—Gas Mark 6).

Tomato and corned beef mould

cooking time   15 minutes

Use same recipe as tomato and fish mould (page 64) but instead of the hard-boiled egg add sliced spring onions and 1 or 2 sliced gherkins or pieces of cucumber.

Tomato cups with cottage cheese

no cooking

1 Scoop out the centres of large tomatoes, fill with cottage cheese, top with cucumber slices and garnish with sliced red pepper.
2 Serve on a bed of lettuce with chicory.

Tomato marrow casserole

cooking time   40—45 minutes

you will need:

1 medium marrow	about ½ oz. butter
8 oz. tomatoes	seasoning
2 large onions	chopped parsley

1 Wipe and peel the marrow.
2 Halve and scoop out the seeds then cut the marrow into slices.
3 Skin the tomatoes. Skin and chop the onion.
4 Put alternate layers of marrow, tomato and onion into a greased casserole and season.
5 Cover with butter and place a tight-fitting lid over the casserole.
6 Bake in a moderate oven (375°F.—Gas Mark 4) for about 40–50 minutes until tender.
7 Garnish with chopped parsley.

Olive-stuffed tomatoes

cooking time   6 minutes

you will need:

8 firm tomatoes	7 olives
2 eggs	sprigs of watercress or
1 oz. grated cheese	parsley to garnish
salt and pepper	lettuce

1 Wipe the tomatoes, cut off their tops and remove the pulp carefully, reserving a little.
2 Scramble the eggs and add the grated cheese and seasonings and 3 chopped olives.
3 Stir the tomato pulp into the egg mixture and fill each tomato with this mixture.
4 Trim the cut-off pieces into a triangle and place on top.
5 Top each with a halved olive and garnish with watercress or parsley.
6 Place on a bed of lettuce leaves, allowing 2 tomatoes per person.

Tomato and fish mould

cooking time   15 minutes

you will need:

½ pint tomato juice	1¼ level dessertspoons
12 oz. flaked cooked	powder gelatine
fish or can tuna fish	2 hard-boiled eggs
or salmon	seasoning

1 Dissolve gelatine in hot tomato juice. Cool.
2 Add fish, sliced eggs and seasoning.
3 Pour into mould and allow to set.
4 Serve with salad. Or as a variation instead of all white fish, add prawns to mould and garnish with prawns and cucumber.

Tomato ring (filled with fresh shrimps)

no cooking

you will need:

1 pint bottled or canned	1 level tablespoon
tomato juice	gelatine
lettuce	1 pint shrimps

1 Dissolve the gelatine in the hot tomato juice, adding extra seasoning if wished.
2 Pour into a ring mould and allow to set.
3 Turn out and fill the middle with shrimps, shredded lettuce.
4 Serve with fresh lemon juice as a dressing.

Tomato and spinach

cooking time   15 minutes

you will need:

4 large tomatoes	1 teaspoon finely chopped
2 heaped tablespoons	onion
cooked spinach	4 slices of cheese cut just
1 oz. margarine	about the size of each
1 tablespoon cream from	tomato
top of the milk	seasoning

1 Try and select tomatoes that will stand upright. Cut a slice from the top of each and scoop out the centre pulp. Cut this finely.
2 Heat the margarine in a saucepan, fry the onion until soft, then mix with the spinach, cream, seasoning and the tomato pulp.
3 Put this into the tomato cases, lay the slices of cheese on top and replace the 'lids'.
4 Put in the centre of a moderate oven (375°F. —Gas Mark 4) and cook for 10 minutes.

Stuffed tomatoes with celery

cooking time   15 minutes

you will need:

4 very large or 8 smaller	1 tiny chopped onion or
tomatoes	chopped chives
4 oz. chopped celery	2 oz. grated cheese
	seasoning

1 Take top off the tomatoes.
2 Scoop out pulp, season cases.
3 Mix chopped pulp with other ingredients.
4 Bake for 15–20 minutes in a moderately hot oven (400°F.—Gas Mark 5).
5 Serve with mushroom sauce (page 44).

Scalloped tomatoes

4–6 Servings

cooking time   40 minutes

you will need:

1 lb. tomatoes	1 small onion, sliced
1 medium size cucumber, peeled and sliced	salt and pepper
	2 oz. grated cheese

1 Place half sliced tomatoes in a large casserole, add half cucumber, onion and season with salt and pepper.
2 Repeat with half remaining tomatoes and remaining cucumber and onion.
3 Top with remaining tomatoes and sprinkle with cheese.
4 Bake in moderately hot oven (400°F.—Gas Mark 5) for 30–40 minutes.

Vegetables and eggs au gratin

cooking time   20 minutes

you will need:

1 lb. boiled small onions	$\frac{1}{2}$ pint egg sauce (page 43)
8 oz. cooked peas	
4 hard-boiled eggs	breadcrumbs, preferably
grated cheese to sprinkle	starch-reduced crumbs

1 Put the onion and peas into a casserole.
2 Put the sliced hard-boiled eggs on top.
3 Pour on the hot sauce.
4 Sprinkle with breadcrumbs then with grated cheese.
5 Brown lightly under the grill.

Stuffed tomato and crabmeat

Recipe as page 64 but use crabmeat instead of celery and add little made mustard and Worcestershire cause.

Vegetable platter with eggs

cooking time   30–40 minutes

you will need:

cooked peas	fried or boiled onion rings
grilled tomatoes	4 poached or fried eggs
grilled mushrooms	tomato sauce (page 44)

1 Dish up the assortment, serve very hot with tomato sauce.
2 The onion rings may be very thick and boiled or fried till pale gold.

Vegetable pie

cooking time   25–30 minutes

you will need:

1–1$\frac{1}{4}$ lb. vegetables*	mushrooms or tomatoes to garnish
$\frac{1}{2}$ pint cheese sauce (page 44)	pepper and salt
	grated cheese

*A few carrots, cauliflower, beans, onions, etc.

1 Cook the vegetables till tender, and make the sauce.
2 Put the vegetables and sauce in layers in a fireproof dish.
3 Sprinkle with a little grated cheese and brown under the grill.

Vegetable egg scramble

cooking time   10 minutes

you will need:

3 eggs	seasoning
1 teacup diced cooked vegetables	$\frac{1}{2}$ oz. margarine or butter

1 Put the margarine into a basin over a pan of hot water and allow to melt.
2 Add the beaten eggs, vegetables and seasoning.
3 Cook steadily, stirring from time to time until set.
4 Top with grated cheese if wished.

Savoury vegetable marrow

cooking time   45 minutes

you will need:

1 medium sized marrow	1 medium can tomatoes
$\frac{1}{2}$ clove garlic	or
2 onions	8 oz. fresh skinned tomatoes
1 oz. fat or 1 tablespoon corn oil	$\frac{1}{4}$ pint water
seasoning	

1 Chop onions and garlic.
2 Fry in hot fat or oil for a few minutes.
3 Add tomatoes and liquid and simmer gently for 10 minutes.
4 Peel and dice marrow, remove seeds, put into onion and tomato mixture with plenty of seasoning.
5 Cover pan and simmer gently for approximately 30 minutes until marrow is tender.

Sugar, sugar substitutes and saccharine
—how to use when on a diet

Sugar substitute or fortified sugar

This is a fine standby for cakes and puddings. It gives much more satisfactory results than using either no sugar at all or an entirely non-caloric sweetener. To make fortified sugar proceed as follows:

1 Crush 24 saccharine tablets to a smooth powder and sift with 8 oz. castor sugar.
2 Store in a tightly lidded jar.
3 8 oz. fortified sugar equal 1 lb. ordinary sugar, so when using fortified sugar in ordinary cake and pudding recipes, use HALF the given weight. For example, if the recipe calls for 8 oz. sugar, use only 4 oz. fortified sugar.
4 If using fortified sugar when stewing fruits, add it AFTER the fruit is cooked.

Saccharine and other sugar substitutes

The modern saccharine is very much better than the old, in that it does not produce such a bitter flavour. You can buy saccharine tablets and these are what I have mentioned in most recipes. You can also buy powdered or liquid saccharine and many people prefer using it in this form. Also on the market are other sugar substitutes. The amount to be used and the method of using will be given on the box.

1 When using saccharine in cakes, puddings and custards, remember to use rather more flavouring (almond or vanilla essence, lemon rind or spices) than usual.
2 With cooked stewed fruits, add the saccharine AFTER the fruit is cooked.
3 Sorbitol or diabetic sweetening products based on Sorbitol are not low-calorie for slimmers.

Sweets, Desserts, Tea Time Drinks Packed Meals

Sweets and desserts for slimmers

Many people are inclined to give up a diet because they cannot bear to be without sweet things.

Obviously, starchy puddings and cakes must be either cut out of the diet completely, or much restricted. On the other hand there is a very wide variety that you CAN have. It is, however, sensible to leave out sugar and use a sugar substitute or saccharine (see following page).

The most slimming sweet that you can serve is fresh fruit, but if people have been in the habit of having a pudding they will, of course, feel the lack of this rather badly.

In the next chapter, therefore, you will find suggestions for a number of delicious low-calorie puddings and desserts. Serve small portions of these, because even though they have been made far more slimming than the ordinary sweet, they still add extra calories after a main dish.

In many cases, if the sweet I have suggested is a very pleasant one, I have given the quantity for 4 servings, so the rest of the family can enjoy it as well. However, since it is obviously unwise to give thin people sweets without sugar, you should compensate for this by serving a well-sweetened custard or cream with their portion.

Upside down pudding

cooking time   25–35 minutes

you will need:

1 lb. fruit—apples, etc.	6 saccharine tablets or
liquid sugar substitute	sugar substitute
2 eggs	2 tablespoons water
very little water	$\frac{3}{4}$ oz. sugar
	3 oz. self-raising flour

1 Put fruit in bottom of greased dish.
2 Dissolve sugar substitute in water and pour over the fruit.
3 If firm plums, apples, etc., cook until nearly tender. With soft fruit this is not necessary.
4 Make sponge. First whisk egg whites until stiff.
5 Whisk in sugar then egg yolks.
6 When thick and creamy fold in sieved flour and saccharine tablets dissolved in water.
7 Spread over the fruit.

8 If the fruit is hot allow approximately 25 minutes in centre of moderate oven (375°F. —Gas Mark 4). If fruit is cold it will take approximately 30–35 minutes.
9 Turn upside down to serve.

Variations:

Ginger upside down pudding

As above but sieve 1–2 teaspoons powdered ginger with flour.
Excellent with apples or pears.

Lemon upside down pudding

As above but add finely grated rind of lemon to the egg yolks, etc.
Blend saccharine with lemon juice instead of water.
Excellent with apricots or mixed fruit.

Orange upside down pudding

As above but add finely grated rind of 1 large or 2 small oranges to egg yolks, etc.
Blend saccharine with orange juice instead of water.
Excellent with rhubarb or pears or mixture of fruits.

Spiced upside down pudding

As above but sieve $1-1\frac{1}{2}$ teaspoons mixed spice with flour.
Excellent with damsons, plums.

Low-calorie sponge puddings

As recipe for the cake, page 77.
This mixture can be steamed but is nicer baked.
Allow approximately 30–35 minutes in a tin or dish in centre of a moderate oven. Serve with orange, lemon or coffee sauce (page 75).

Variations:

Orange sponge

Recipe as low calorie sponge (page 77) but dissolve the finely grated rind of 1 orange with the egg yolks and blend the saccharine tablets with orange juice instead of water.

Lemon sponge

As orange sponge but use lemon.

Baked egg custard

cooking time $1\frac{1}{2}$ hours

you will need:

3 eggs	2–3 saccharine tablets
1 pint milk	or sugar substitute
	grated nutmeg

1 Beat the eggs and add the milk and saccharine.
2 Strain into an ovenproof dish and sprinkle with grated nutmeg.
3 Place in a dish of cold water and cook in a slow oven for $1\frac{1}{2}$ hours (275–300°F.—Gas Mark 2).

Variation:

Coffee baked custard

As above, but use $\frac{3}{4}$ pint milk and $\frac{1}{4}$ pint strong coffee.

Fluffy coffee custard

cooking time $1\frac{1}{2}$ hours

you will need:

$\frac{1}{4}$ pint strong coffee	$\frac{3}{4}$ pint milk
3 eggs	2–3 saccharine tablets

1 Beat the egg yolks with the milk and coffee.
2 Add saccharine tablets.
3 Fold in stiffly beaten egg whites.
4 Place in a dish of cold water and cook in a slow oven for $1\frac{1}{2}$ hours (275–300°F.—Gas Mark 2).

Variation:

Fluffy custard

As above, but pour the milk over the egg yolks only and add saccharine.
Fold in stiffly beaten egg whites.
Bake as before.

Baked vanilla cream

cooking time   40 minutes

you will need:

1 pint milk	2 eggs
2 crushed saccharine	$\frac{1}{2}$ teaspoon vanilla essence
tablets or sugar	grated cinnamon or
substitute	nutmeg

1 Mix milk and beaten eggs.
2 Add saccharine and essence.
3 Pour into an oven dish.

4 Dust top with spice.
5 Set dish in a pan of water and bake in a very moderate oven (350°F.—Gas Mark 3) until lightly set, about 40 minutes.

Rhubarb amber

cooking time   40–45 minutes

you will need:

1 lb. rhubarb	3 saccharine tablets or
2 eggs	sugar substitute
1 oz. margarine	approximately
1 oz. sugar	1 tablespoon water
	2 or 3 glacé cherries

1 Put the rhubarb and water into a saucepan and cook steadily until the rhubarb is soft.
2 Beat mixture until smooth.
3 Add the margarine, dissolved saccharine tablets and the beaten egg yolks.
4 Pour fruit mixture into a dish, set for about 25 minutes in a moderately hot oven (400°F.—Gas Mark 5).
5 Beat the egg whites until very stiff, fold in the sugar and set the meringue for about 15 minutes in a very moderate oven (350°F.—Gas Mark 3).
As this sweet is much nicer hot than cold, there is no need to set the meringue very slowly.

Sweet omelette soufflé

cooking time   7–10 minutes

you will need:

2 eggs	1 tablespoon jam, use
few drops liquid sweetener	low calorie jam if
or sugar	possible
grated lemon rind	salt
a little butter	

1 Put the yolks into a basin with the lemon rind or other flavouring and mix well with a spoon until of a pale creamy consistency.
2 Whip the whites, with a pinch of salt added to them, to a very stiff froth and mix them very lightly into the yolks with a spoon. Do not stir more than is necessary.
3 Put the mixture into a well-greased omelette pan and put in a brisk oven from 7–10 minutes, until of a pale brown colour.
4 Serve quickly on a hot dish.
A little stewed fruit may be used instead of jam or the omelette may be served plain.

Fresh grapefruit jelly

cooking time   5 minutes

you will need:

1 large grapefruit	1 pint water
2 level dessertspoons	3–4 saccharine tablets or
powdered gelatine	sugar substitute

Grate the 'zest' from the grapefruit. Be careful not to use any white pith otherwise you will make the jelly bitter.

Put the grapefruit rind with the water into a saucepan and simmer gently for a good 5 minutes then strain through muslin.

Soften the gelatine in the grapefruit juice, then pour on the boiling grapefruit juice.

Add sugar substitute or saccharine to taste.

Pour either into a mould to set or into glasses or grapefruit halves and when set decorate with slices of fresh fruit.

This will be enough for 4 small moulds.

Fresh lemon jelly

cooking time   5 minutes

you will need:

3 lemons
2 level dessertspoons
  powdered gelatine

water
3–4 saccharine tablets
  or sugar substitute

1 Grate the 'zest' from the lemon. Be careful not to use any white pith otherwise you will make the jelly bitter.
2 Put lemon rind with a good $\frac{3}{4}$ pint of water into a saucepan and simmer gently for a good 5 minutes, then strain through muslin.
3 Soften the gelatine in the lemon juice, then pour on the boiling lemon liquid. You should now have 1 pint liquid in all, if not then add a little water.
4 Add sugar substitute or saccharine to taste.
5 Pour either into a mould to set or into glasses or lemon halves and when set decorate with slices of fresh fruit.
6 This will be enough for 4 small moulds.

Lemon snow

ingredients as above plus 2 egg whites

1 When the jelly is nearly set FOLD in the stiffly beaten egg white.
2 You may find you need a little extra saccharine.
3 Put into 4 glasses.

Fresh orange jelly

cooking time   5 minutes

you will need:

2 large oranges
1 pint water
2 level dessertspoons
  powdered gelatine

few drops orange
  colouring (not essential)
3–4 saccharine tablets
  or sugar substitute

1 Grate the 'zest' from the orange. Be careful not to use any white pith otherwise you will make the jelly bitter.
2 Put the orange rind with the water into a saucepan and simmer gently for a good 5 minutes then strain through muslin.
3 Soften the gelatine in the orange juice, then pour on the boiling orange liquid.
4 Add sugar substitute or saccharine to taste together with the colouring.
5 Pour either into a mould to set or into glasses or orange halves and when set decorate with slices of fresh fruit.
6 This will be enough for 4 small moulds.

Lemon and orange jelly

no cooking

you will need:

juice and rind of 2 lemons
juice and rind of 2 oranges
1 orange

1 tablespoon powdered
  gelatine
$\frac{1}{2}$ pint water
2–3 saccharine tablets

1 Simmer the fruit rind in the water for 5 minutes, then strain.
2 Dissolve gelatine and saccharine in this.
3 Add fruit juices and, if necessary, more water to give 1 pint.
4 Remove pieces of fruit from the third orange and add to the jelly.
5 Set in 4 individual moulds.
6 The rest of the family can top their jelly with cream.
7 Do not have too large portions of jelly, as gelatine is fairly high in calories.

Three-fruit jelly

cooking time   5 minutes

you will need:

1 tangerine
1 orange
1 lemon
1 pint water

2 level dessertspoons
  powdered gelatine
3–4 saccharine tablets
  or sugar substitute

1 Grate the 'zest' from the tangerine, orange and lemon. Be careful not to use any white pith otherwise you will make the jelly bitter.
2 Put the rind with the water into a saucepan and simmer gently for a good 5 minutes then strain through muslin.
3 Soften the gelatine in the juice, then pour on the boiling liquid.
4 Add sugar substitute or saccharine to taste.
5 Pour either into a mould to set or into glasses and when set decorate with slices of fresh fruit.
6 This will be enough for 4 small moulds.

Gooseberry and lemon jelly

cooking time   10 minutes

you will need:

12 oz. green gooseberries	$\frac{1}{2}$ pint water
1 lemon-flavoured jelly	2 saccharine tablets or
cream to decorate	sugar substitute

1 Simmer the gooseberries until the fruit is soft, lift out a few gooseberries for decoration and continue cooking the remainder until a pulp. Add saccharine.
2 Rub through a sieve and measure the pulp and syrup.
3 Add enough water to give nearly $1\frac{1}{4}$ pints altogether.
4 Dissolve the lemon jelly in this hot mixture and put into a mould.
5 Turn out and decorate with cream and the whole fruit.

Egg jelly

2 Servings

cooking time   5–10 minutes

you will need:

1 egg	1 dessertspoon powdered
1 lemon	gelatine
good oz. sugar	

1 Grate the lemon rind finely and simmer in slightly less than $\frac{1}{2}$ pint water for 5 minutes.
2 Strain and dissolve the sugar in the liquid, then add the juice of the lemon. You should have about $\frac{1}{2}$ pint liquid altogether.
3 Add the gelatine and beaten egg and cook over a glimmer of heat until the egg mixture has thickened.
4 Pour into rinsed mould and allow to set.
5 If preferred, the egg can be added uncooked, in which case use slightly less water and make sure the gelatine is dissolved before adding the egg.

Variation:

Fluffy egg jelly

Make as above, but use just the yolk of the egg at the beginning. When the jelly is just beginning to thicken stir in the stiffly beaten egg white. Allow to set.

Milk jellies

cooking time   few minutes heating

you will need:

$\frac{3}{4}$ pint milk	$\frac{1}{4}$ pint water
fruit jelly	

1 Dissolve fruit flavoured jelly cubes or crystals in $\frac{1}{4}$ pint water (boiling).

2 Add the cold milk when the jelly has cooled to prevent curdling.

Variation:

To make a less 'solid' sweet turn into mock mousse by folding in the stiffly beaten white of an egg just before jelly has set. Pour into 4 glasses.

Lemon milk jelly

cooking time   5 minutes

you will need:

1 large lemon	2 level dessertspoons
$\frac{1}{4}$ pint water	powdered gelatine
$\frac{3}{4}$ pint milk	3–4 saccharine tablets
	or sugar substitute

1 Grate the 'zest' from the lemons. Be careful not to use any white pith otherwise you will make the jelly bitter.
2 Put the lemon rind with the water into a saucepan and simmer gently for a good 5 minutes then strain through muslin.
3 Add the lemon juice to the liquid and measure. You should now have a good $\frac{1}{4}$ pint.
4 Reheat with the gelatine, stirring until dissolved.
5 Add the saccharine or sugar substitute. Cool slightly, and then whisk in the cold milk.
6 Pour into a large mould or 4 small ones.

Orange milk jelly

cooking time   5 minutes

you will need:

1 large orange	3–4 saccharine tablets
just under $\frac{1}{4}$ pint water	or sugar substitute
$\frac{3}{4}$ pint milk	2 level dessertspoons
	powdered gelatine

1 Grate the 'zest' from the orange. Be careful not to use any white pith otherwise you will make the jelly bitter.
2 Put the orange rind with the water into a saucepan and simmer gently for a good 5 minutes then strain through muslin.
3 Add the orange juice to the liquid and measure. You should now have a good $\frac{1}{4}$ pint.
4 Reheat with the gelatine, stirring until dissolved.
5 Add the saccharine or sugar substitute. Cool slightly and then whisk in the cold milk.
6 Pour into a large mould or 4 small ones.

Tangerine milk jelly

cooking time   5 minutes

you will need:

2 tangerines	$\frac{3}{4}$ pint milk
just under $\frac{1}{4}$ pint water	2 level dessertspoons
3–4 saccharine tablets or	powdered gelatine
sugar substitute	

Grate the 'zest' from the tangerines. Be careful not to use any white pith, otherwise you will make the jelly bitter.

Put the tangerine rind with the water into a saucepan and simmer gently for a good 5 minutes then strain through muslin.

Add the tangerine juice to the liquid and measure. You should now have a good $\frac{1}{4}$ pint. Reheat with the gelatine, stirring until dissolved.

Add the saccharine or sugar substitute. Cool slightly and then whisk in the cold milk.

Pour into a large mould or 4 small ones.

boiling water until the mixture thickens, coating the back of a wooden spoon.
4 Cool slightly, add the reserved orange gelatine liquid.
5 Fold in the sieved cottage cheese.
6 Stir in the crushed saccharines or sugar substitute, adjusting sweetness to taste.
7 Fold in the stiffly whisked egg white.
8 When the jelly is set break it up with a wire whisk and arrange it in layers in tall glasses with the orange cream decorating top of each glass with a cube or spoonful of the jelly.

Jellied apple mould

cooking time   30 minutes

you will need:

1¼ lb. apples	3–4 saccharine tablets
2 tablespoons hot water	or sugar substitute
½ pint water	¾ oz. gelatine
grated rind of ½ lemon	cochineal

1 Wash the fruit, do not peel or cut up, and cook gently in water.
2 When the apples have softened, press through a sieve.
3 Heat a pint of this pulp with the lemon rind then stir in the gelatine (previously dissolved in the hot water), and add enough cochineal to colour a delicate pink, together with saccharine tablets.
4 Rinse out a mould with cold water and pour in the apple mixture.
5 Turn out when set.

Orange cream desserts

cooking time   15 minutes

you will need:

Orange jelly
½ oz. powder gelatine
¾ pint orange juice
¼ pint water

Cream
2 eggs
¼ pint milk

finely grated rind of orange
8 oz. sieved cottage cheese
about 3 saccharines or sugar substitute

1 Soften the gelatine in the water.
2 Strain and heat the orange juice and add the softened gelatine, stirring until dissolved. Reserve 3 or 4 tablespoons of this jelly mixture to add to the cream and chill remainder until set.
3 Beat 1 egg and 1 egg yolk with the milk and orange rind and stir in a double pan over

Orange chiffon cream

cooking time   15 minutes

you will need:

3 eggs	2 teaspoons gelatine
grated rind of 1 orange	about 8 saccharine
juice of 2 large oranges	tablets dissolved in
juice of ½ lemon	3 tablespoons hot water

1 Beat egg yolks until creamy.
2 Add orange juice, lemon juice and orange rind and cook over boiling water until beginning to thicken.
3 Add dissolved gelatine and saccharine and stir well.
4 Taste and if preferred sweeten further.
5 Set aside to cool and when beginning to set whisk in stiffly beaten egg whites.
6 Pile mixture into individual glasses and decorate with a light sprinkling of chopped nuts or shredded coconut.
7 Can be served with low-calorie cream (page 75).

Gooseberry mould

cooking time   15–20 minutes

you will need:

1 lb. fresh gooseberries	4 saccharine tablets or
2 eggs	sugar substitute
½ oz. gelatine	½ pint milk
a little green colouring	nuts

1 Stew the gooseberries and a little water to prevent sticking. Add sugar substitute. When cooked and soft rub through a sieve.
2 Whisk the yolks of eggs and add the milk and gelatine, stir in a double saucepan until it thickens.
3 Cool, mix in the gooseberry purée and tint.
4 Whisk the egg whites stiffly and fold into the mixture.
5 Pour into a mould.
6 Turn out and decorate with few nuts.

Variation:
Blackcurrant mould

As previous recipe, but using blackcurrants in place of the gooseberries. Be very careful the blackcurrant purée is well thickened before adding to the egg and milk mixture.

Coffee whip

cooking time	few minutes only

you will need:

2 egg whites	¼ pint strong coffee
½ oz. powdered gelatine	1 tablespoon single cream
½ pint milk	2–3 saccharine tablets
a few almonds	or sugar substitute

1 Dissolve powdered gelatine in black coffee.
2 Warm the milk and sweeten with the crushed saccharine tablets or sugar substitute.
3 Add dissolved gelatine.
4 Allow to cool and when beginning to set whisk in the stiffly beaten egg whites and the cream.
5 Chill and serve sprinkled with slivers of almonds.

Coffee sponge

cooking time	few minutes heating

you will need:

2 egg whites	3 saccharine tablets or
1 pint coffee	sugar substitute
	½ oz. powdered gelatine

1 First make a pint of coffee.
2 Strain and dissolve gelatine and powdered sugar substitute to taste.
3 Allow to set lightly and fold in stiffly beaten egg whites.
4 Pile into glasses.

Apple fluff

cooking time	15 minutes

you will need:

10–12 oz. very thick	desiccated coconut
apple purée*	¼ pint yoghourt
1 tablespoon honey	grated rind and juice of
1–2 saccharine tablets	1 lemon
or sugar substitute	2–3 egg whites

*Made from approximately 1 lb. apples and a little water but NO sugar.

1 Whisk honey and crushed saccharines or sugar substitute into apple.
2 Add yoghourt and grated rind and juice of lemon.
3 Beat whites of the eggs until stiff but not dry and fold into apple purée.

4 Pile into large bowl or individual glasses, chill and top with toasted desiccated coconut just before serving.

Variation:
Apple ginger fluff

Recipe as above but add 1 good teaspoon of powdered ginger to the apple purée and decorate with tiny pieces of crystallised ginger, instead of coconut.

Apricot fluff

Recipe as above, but use 12 oz. thick, fresh apricot purée, and add chopped kernels.

Plum fluff

Recipe as above, but use 12 oz. thick plum purée, and flavour with a little almond essence.

Golden fluff

cooking time	10–15 minutes

you will need:

1 pint milk	2 dessertspoons powdered
2 eggs	gelatine
4 saccharine tablets	2 dessertspoons lemon
or sugar substitute	(or orange) juice

1 Separate yolks from whites of eggs.
2 Put the yolks and milk either into a basin over a pan of very hot water or into a double saucepan and cook slowly until mixture thickens.
3 Remove from the heat and allow to cool slightly.
4 Add half the crushed saccharine tablets or sugar substitute, stirring well.
5 Soften the gelatine in the lemon or orange juice, then pour on the hot custard. This should not be added when boiling.
6 Pour into a rinsed mould or moulds and allow to set.
7 When quite firm turn out.
8 Beat the egg whites very stiffly. Fold in the rest of the crushed saccharine tablets or sugar substitute and pile on top of the jelly.
9 Serve soon after decorating with egg white.

Fruit 'creams'

cooking time	few minutes heating

you will need:

1 fruit-flavoured jelly	½ pint fruit purée
just under ½ pint milk	(unsweetened)

1 Make jelly with $\frac{1}{4}$ pint boiling water, add fruit pulp and milk.
2 Put into mould to set, or into glasses.
If setting in glasses a full $\frac{1}{2}$ pint milk can be used.

Fruit snows

cooking time   15 minutes

you will need:

1 lb. fruit	4 saccharine tablets or
little water	sugar substitute
2 eggs	

1 Cook fruit with very little liquid and sugar substitute.
2 Rub through a sieve or beat into a smooth pulp.
3 Add the stiffly beaten whites of the eggs. These are delicious.

Apple snow

cooking time   10–12 minutes

you will need:

1$\frac{1}{2}$ lb. apples	strip of lemon rind
2 egg whites	glacé cherries
3–4 saccharines	

1 Peel and slice the apples and cook them to a pulp with the lemon rind and a very little water.
2 Add the saccharines. Cool.
3 Stiffly whisk the egg whites and fold into the apple mixture.
4 Place in the bottom of a dish, and decorate with a few glacé cherries.

Blackcurrant and raspberry snow

cooking time   1$\frac{1}{2}$ hours

you will need:

8 oz. blackcurrants	**For the ring:**
8 oz. raspberries	1 pint milk
3 saccharine tablets	3 egg yolks and 1 whole
3 egg whites	egg
	2–3 saccharine tablets

1 Beat egg yolks, whole egg and saccharine together, pour over the warmed milk and mix thoroughly.
2 Pour into a greased ring mould or stand a tin in the centre of a larger one to give the shape of a ring.
3 Bake until set in a very slow oven (275–300°F. —Gas Mark 1–2).
4 Cool slightly, then turn out.
5 Cook the blackcurrants with saccharine to taste until soft.
6 Cool, then add the mashed raw raspberries and the stiffly beaten egg whites.
7 Pile in the centre of the custard ring.

Fruit fool

cooking time   10–15 minutes

you will need:

12 oz. fruit	3–4 saccharine tablets
very little water	or sugar substitute
	$\frac{1}{2}$ pint yoghourt

1 Cook plums, damsons, apple or other fruit with very little water until thick pulp.
2 Add saccharine or sugar substitute when cooking completed.
3 Mix with an equal quantity of yoghourt.
4 Pile into 4 glasses.

Variation:
Rich fruit fool

As above, but instead of all yoghourt use little cream with yoghourt.

Plum fool

cooking time   15 minutes

you will need:

1 lb. plums	3 saccharine tablets
$\frac{1}{4}$ pint yoghourt	or sugar substitute
glacé cherries	2 or 3 tablespoons water

1 Simmer the plums with the water and when soft add saccharine tablets or sugar substitute.
2 Remove the stones and either rub through a sieve or beat into a smooth pulp.
3 Beat together into yoghourt.
4 Put into 4 glasses and allow to cool.
5 Decorate on top with cherries.

Variations:
Blackcurrant fool

Simmer 12 oz. blackcurrants without water, for you must have a very thick fruit pulp. Rub through a sieve and allow the fruit to get QUITE cold before adding to yoghourt.

Damson fool

As blackcurrant fool.

Gooseberry fool

Use rather green fruit to give a good flavour and the same amount of water as for plums. This means stirring the fruit well to begin with, so that it does not burn. Sieve to get rid of pips and skins.

Rhubarb fool

Use 12 oz. fruit but simmer in a covered dish in a low oven, so that you need add no water at all. Either sieve or beat with a wooden spoon to a smooth purée.

Apricot delights

cooking time   few minutes

you will need:

1 lb. apricots	1 oz. chopped walnuts
3 saccharine tablets or	3 oz. cottage cheese
sugar substitute	grated rind of 1 orange
stick of cinnamon	

1 Place apricots into a pan containing just enough water to prevent them sticking.
2 Add a stick of cinnamon, cover and cook gently until tender.
3 Stir in saccharine tablets or sugar substitute.
4 Cool and cut in two, removing stones.
5 Sandwich apricot cups together with a mixture of cottage cheese, grated orange rind and chopped walnuts, letting cheese mixture show at the sides.
6 Pour a light trickle of single cream over each before serving, if diet will permit.

Junket

2 Servings

cooking time   few minutes

you will need:

½ pint milk (or milk	1 teaspoon sugar or
and cream)	1 saccharine
1 teaspoon rennet	flavouring if desired

1 Heat the milk and sugar to blood heat, stir in the rennet. Also add flavouring at this point, if desired.
2 Pour into two individual glass dishes and leave to set in a warm place. If using saccharine, crush and add to warm milk.

Variation:

Coffee junket

2 Servings

As above, but dissolve 2 teaspoons powdered coffee in the milk.

Frothy sweet yoghourt

cooking time   few minutes

you will need:

¼ pint yoghourt	4–6 saccharine tablets
2 eggs	or sugar substitute
nutmeg or cinnamon	

1 Warm yoghourt in a basin standing in a pan of hot water.
2 Beat in the egg yolks and cook, stirring for 3 minutes.
3 Add crushed saccharine tablets or sugar substitute.
4 Cool and fold in whites whisked until stiff.
5 Serve cold in 4 glasses dusted with nutmeg or cinnamon.
This is very sweet and so an excellent dish to serve when the diet appears to be becoming over strict and you 'pine' for sugar.

Berry fruit mousse

1 Serving

no cooking

you will need:

4 oz. raspberries	1 saccharine tablet
1 egg white	

1 Crush raspberries, or strawberries, through a sieve.
2 Dissolve a saccharine tablet in very little warm water and add to fruit purée.
3 Whisk 1 egg white until stiff, fold it carefully on to the purée.
4 Pile into a dish.
5 Decorate with whole fruit.

Fruit Sorbet

no cooking

you will need:

½ pint thick fruit purée	2–3 crushed saccharine
2 egg whites	tablets or sugar
	substitute

1 Mix thick fruit purée with the stiffly beaten whites of eggs and crushed saccharine to sweeten.
2 Put into the freezing trays of your refrigerator and freeze until just firm.

Fresh fruit salad

no cooking

you will need:

2 dessert pears	juice of 1 lemon or
1 dessert apple	orange
1 orange or tangerine	1 bottle gooseberries
3 dessert plums or apricots	or other fruit
4 oz. white and black	1 peach
grapes mixed	2–3 saccharine tablets or
a few cherries	sugar substitute
1 banana	¼ pint water

1 Prepare the pears and remove the centres with the aid of a teaspoon.
2 Peel and core the apple, and cut up into sections.
3 Peel the orange or tangerine and divide into segments.

4 Cut the plums and the peach in half and remove the stones, then slice into convenient-sized pieces.

5 Place all these fruits in a chilled bowl, together with the grapes, sliced banana, cherries and gooseberries.

6 Sweeten ¼ pint water with saccharine or sugar substitute to taste, add the lemon juice and pour over the fruit.

Fruit mélange

2–3 Servings

no cooking

you will need:

2 slices pineapple	½ grapefruit
1 tablespoon seeded raisins	sprinkle of walnuts (or poppy seed or desiccated coconut)
1 tablespoon dry sherry	
1 orange	

1 Chop fruit into small pieces and blend with the sherry.

2 Chill in a covered dish.

3 Serve topped with a sprinkle of nuts or seed or coconut.

Can be topped with low calorie cream (page 75), leaving out the fruit in this.

Cottage cheese fruit cream

no cooking

you will need:

2 tablespoons cottage cheese	1 tablespoon fruit (such as dessert prunes, raisins, dried apricots, fresh pineapple, seeded grapes)
few drops vanilla essence	
cinnamon	
desiccated coconut	

1 Combine chopped fruit with cheese and flavouring.

2 Dust with cinnamon and desiccated coconut.

Grapefruit cups

no cooking

you will need:

2 oranges	2 saccharine tablets or sugar substitute
2 grapefruit	
1 oz. nuts	1 tablespoon lemon juice

1 Prepare the grapefruit as usual.

2 Remove the pulp and discard the thin skin round each section.

3 Place the flesh in a bowl, add flesh from oranges and the saccharine tablets, dissolved in lemon juice.

4 Leave in a cold place for about 1 hour.

5 Add some nuts to the grapefruit flesh and return the mixture to the cases.

Spiced apple cream

no cooking

you will need:

4 crisp dessert apples	2 saccharine tablets or sugar substitute
¼ pint yoghurt	
cinnamon	lemon or grapefruit juice
sesame or poppy seeds	

1 Wash, core, but don't peel the apples. Cut in thin wedges.

2 Sprinkle with lemon or grapefruit juice.

3 Whisk yoghourt with saccharine tablets or sugar substitute.

4 Spoon over the apples then dust with cinnamon and sprinkle with seeds.

Orange sauce

cooking time   15 minutes

you will need:

grated rind of 2 oranges	2 level teaspoons arrowroot
juice of 2 oranges	
6 tablespoons water	2 saccharine tablets or sugar substitute

1 Simmer orange peel in water for nearly 10 minutes.

2 Blend arrowroot with orange juice.

3 Stir into pan and cook until thick and clear.

4 Add saccharine tablets or sugar substitute.

Variation:

Lemon sauce

As recipe above but you may need extra saccharines. Use lemons instead of oranges.

Coffee sauce

cooking time   5 minutes

you will need:

½ pint coffee	2 saccharine tablets or sugar substitute
2 level teaspoons arrowroot	

1 Blend arrowroot with coffee.

2 Boil until thick and clear.

3 Add saccharine tablets.

Low-calorie cream filling

no cooking

you will need:

4 oz. cottage cheese	1 saccharine tablet or sugar substitute
fruit, nuts or seed for flavouring	

1 Rub cottage cheese through a sieve.

2 Sweeten with the crushed saccharine tablet.

3 Chopped nuts or toasted sesame seeds or chopped, well-drained pineapple or sliced strawberries can be added to taste.

Pineapple and grapefruit baskets

no cooking

you will need:

2 good-sized grapefruit
approximately 5 oz. diced
  fresh pineapple

little sugar*
cherries
mint

*Omit sugar entirely or use little diluted sugar substitute.

1 Cut the grapefruit into halves through the centre, remove the pulp and mix with the pineapple, and any juice from pineapple.
2 Sweeten to taste, pile back into grapefruit cases and decorate with cherries and mint sprigs.
3 Put a handle of pineapple skin or grapefruit skin over the top if wished.
4 In cold weather the mixture of pineapple and grapefruit can be heated. Top with a little sugar, butter and spice and heat.

Pineapple berry roundabout

4–6 Servings

no cooking

you will need:

fresh pineapple
1–2 crushed saccharine
  tablets or sugar
  substitute

fresh strawberries or
  raspberries
6–8 oz. cottage cheese
1 tablespoon milk or
  yoghourt

1 Peel, core and cut fresh pineapple into rings.
2 Sieve cottage cheese, blend with milk or yoghourt and crushed saccharine tablets or sugar substitute.
3 Top each pineapple ring with a tablespoon of sieved cottage cheese and top with a spoonful of fresh strawberries or raspberries when in season.

Melon basket

no cooking

you will need:

ripe melon
fresh fruit

lemon or orange juice
sugar substitute

1 Cut a slice off top of melon and scoop out the seeds, with some of the pulp. Turn the melon upside down to drain, whilst preparing the filling.
2 Cut the melon pulp up into small pieces and mix with fresh fruit (raspberries, strawberries or redcurrants are probably the best fruits to choose).
3 Pile the fruit and melon mixture into the melon, pour on juice, sweetened with sugar substitute and replace the lid.

Melon boats

no cooking

you will need:

1 melon
1 grapefruit
few plums

sprigs of mint
2 pears

1 Cut rather thick slices of melon, then cut fruit from peel and dice neatly.
2 Mix melon with pieces of grapefruit, few diced plums (or oranges), diced pear.
3 Arrange the mixed fruit on the boat shaped sections of melon.
4 Decorate with sprigs of mint.

Melon 'sandwiches'

no cooking

you will need:

slices of melon
cottage cheese
chopped nuts

chopped, drained
  pineapple
chopped preserved
  ginger

1 Combine cheese, nuts, ginger and pineapple.
2 Use as filling between thin slices of melon.
3 For a gay effect make three-tiered 'sandwiches', alternating green honeydew and yellow cantaloup melon.

Teatime tips for slimmers

If you have been in the habit of having a really good tea, with plenty of bread and butter, cakes, sweet tea, this may have contributed to your over-weight.

It is certain that this is the meal where you must make quite a sacrifice.

1 If you have used a considerable amount of milk during the day in cooking, try to cut down on the milk in your tea.
2 Use saccharine tablets or sugar substitute.
3 Either give yourself one piece of bread and butter or crispbread or rusks or a couple of starch-reduced rolls. You may prefer a scraping of butter on these, unless, of course, your diet allows a fairly generous amount of butter.
4 Beware of jams, jellies, honey, etc. You will find recipes for low-calorie jams on page 78.
5 Try to develop a taste for something savoury.
6 A tomato or some watercress helps to fill out the meal.
7 Cakes really should be avoided on a strict diet, but in case this makes you too unhappy there is a recipe for low calorie sponge on page 77.

Sugar substitutes in baking

For the types of sugar substitutes available, and methods of using them in baking, see page 66.

Crispbreads

cooking time   45 minutes

These are light and crisp and taste very good. Appearance improves with practice.

you will need:

4 oz. soft white plain flour	1 level tablespoon dried yeast OR 1 oz. fresh yeast
1 teaspoon sugar	
2 oz. brown flour	$\frac{1}{2}$ pint warm water
1 teaspoon salt	1 tablespoon olive or corn oil

1 Rub the yeast into the flour.
2 Make a rather thin smooth batter with the water.
3 Stand till frothy, about 10 minutes, in warm place.
4 Stir in oil.
5 Pour the light, frothy batter in a circle on to baking sheets, greased and thickly floured with brown flour. (Thin baking sheets are better than thick heavy ones).
6 Tilt the baking sheets to run the batter thinly over.
7 Stand aside till the surface looks bubbly. Dredge tops with brown flour.
8 Bake in a very slow oven (300°F.—Gas Mark 2) on top shelf. After 15 minutes take the baking sheets out and mark the crispbread in pieces with a pastry wheel or a serrated knife.
9 Prick with a fork.
10 Return to *middle shelf* of oven for about 30 minutes. The crispbreads will be more evenly cooked if the side ones are moved to the middle at half time.
11 Turn off the heat and leave to dry off in the oven with door ajar. Don't forget, it is ESSENTIAL when making crispbreads to have a thin batter with lots of yeast. Careful low-temperature baking and the drying off in the oven are also very important.
12 Store when quite cold in an airtight tin.

Variation:

Substitute 1 oz. rolled oats for 1 oz. flour. Add 1 teaspoon caraway seeds.

Tea time rusks

cooking time   15 minutes

you will need:

4 oz. flour (with plain flour use 1 teaspoon baking powder)	good pinch salt
	1 dessertspoon sugar (a little more can be used if desired)
1 oz. margarine	
milk to mix	

1 Sieve the ingredients together. Rub in margarine.
2 Add the sugar and just enough liquid to make a firm dough.
3 Roll out and cut into rounds $\frac{2}{3}$-inch thick.
4 Put on to ungreased baking sheet and bake for a good 5 minutes in a hot oven (450°F.—Gas Mark 7).
5 Remove the trays from the oven and split the rusks through the centre.
6 Put onto the trays, cut side down. You will, of course, need more baking trays since you now have twice the original number of rounds.
7 Bake for a further 10 minutes in a moderate oven (375°F.—Gas Mark 4).
8 Cool on rack and put into tin the moment they are quite cold.

Variation:

Cheese rusks

cooking time   15 minutes

As above but use no sugar and 1 oz. grated cheese, preferably Parmesan.

Low-calorie sponge cake

cooking time   20 minutes

you will need:

3 egg whites	4 oz. self-raising flour
1 oz. sugar	8 saccharine tablets or equivalent in sugar substitute
3 egg yolks	
$\frac{1}{4}$ teaspoon vanilla essence	

1 Whisk egg whites until stiff.
2 Whisk in sugar and then egg yolks and essence.
3 When thick and creamy fold in sifted flour then fold in saccharine tablets (dissolved in 3 tablespoons hot water).
4 Turn into two 7- or 8-inch greased sandwich tins.
5 Bake in a moderate oven (375°F.—Gas Mark 4) for about 20 minutes.
6 Cool on a wire tray and sandwich with low-calorie cream filling (page 75).
NOTE: This recipe can also be used as a pudding (page 67). Sugar plays an important part in lightening a sponge so this recipe does not produce so light a result as one using all sugar.

Tip to dieters

A small portion of low-calorie sponge cake is approximately 100 calories.

Butter in your slimming diet

The amount of butter you are allowed will depend on the type of diet you are following. However, if you are just attempting a general slimming campaign you really should allow yourself not much more than $\frac{1}{2}$ oz. butter per day. This includes the butter you will use for spreading and in cooking.

You make the butter go further if you turn some of it into a savoury spread (see following recipe).

Low-calorie savoury spreads

Anchovy butter: Add a few drops of anchovy essence to the butter.

Cheese butter: Add a little finely grated cheese to the butter.

Carrot butter: Add grated carrot mixed with a tiny knob of butter and a little seasoning and perhaps some grated cheese.

Parsley butter: Add finely chopped parsley and a squeeze of lemon juice to the butter.

Watercress butter: Add lots of chopped watercress, a squeeze of lemon juice to the butter.

Apple curd

cooking time   20–30 minutes

you will need:

12 oz. cooking apples, peeled, cored and cut up	2 tablespoons lemon juice
2 tablespoons water	2 oz. butter (not margarine)
thin strip lemon rind	2–3 saccharine tablets
2 egg yolks	or sugar substitute

1 Cook the apples till tender with water, lemon rind and juice.
2 Remove rind and rub the rest through a sieve.
3 Put this purée into the top of a double pan and add the butter, saccharine tablets or sugar substitute and beaten yolks.
4 Stir over gently boiling water until the yolks thicken.
5 Remove from heat at once and pour into small pots.
6 Cover immediately.
NOTE: As this curd will not keep good for a very long while, it is best made in small quantities. 'Windfalls' can be used for it.

Economical sugarless lemon curd

cooking time   20 minutes

you will need:

juice of 2 medium-sized lemons	1$\frac{1}{4}$ oz. margarine
3 saccharine tablets	1 small egg

1 Stand basin in a pan of boiling water.
2 Melt margarine in the basin and add crushed saccharine tablets.
3 Add lemon juice and then the egg well beaten.
4 Stir over heat until the mixture thickens.
5 Pot and keep covered with a piece of muslin instead of a lid.
NOTE: This curd will keep for at least a week.

Sugarless lemon curd

cooking time   25 minutes

you will need:

2 oz. butter	3 large eggs
grated rind and juice 2 lemons	3 saccharine tablets
	1 teaspoon warm water

1 Put the butter, lemon juice and rind (take care to grate only top yellow from lemons) into a double saucepan.
2 Heat until butter is melted, add beaten eggs.
3 Cook, without boiling, until hot.
4 Cool slightly then add saccharines dissolved in water.
5 Taste, and if desired, more saccharines can be added.
NOTE: Store in a cool place. This keeps for some days.

Sugarless jam

cooking time   15 minutes

you will need:

1 lb. fruit	$\frac{1}{2}$ oz. powdered gelatine
a little water	2 tablespoons water
8–10 saccharine tablets	(hot)
1 tablespoon hot water	

1 Simmer fruit with a little water until soft.
2 Crush saccharine tablets dissolved in the hot water, add to HOT but not boiling fruit.
3 Add the gelatine dissolved in the hot water.
4 Stir briskly for several minutes, pour into small jars with firmly fitting tops and seal.
5 Stand in a cool place.
NOTE: This will keep for some days.
To make jam that will keep for a longer period, pour very hot jam into hot bottling jar. Seal down, giving screw band half turn back. Stand in a pan of boiling water and boil briskly for 5 minutes. Lift out and tighten screw band. Test for seal next day by seeing if lid is tight.

Sugarless Seville orange marmalade

cooking time   1½ hours

you will need:

1 lb. Seville oranges (3 medium sized)
1 oz. powdered gelatine
2 pints water
¼ pint hot water
2 tablespoons hot water
18–20 saccharine tablets

1 Shred the orange peel, discarding SOME of the white pith.
2 Tie pips in a muslin bag.
3 Put juice in a separate container.
4 Soak peel and pips in the 2 pints water for 12–24 hours.
5 Simmer gently until peel is very soft, adding the pips and juice.
6 Remove bag of pips. Dissolve gelatine in the ¼ pint hot water and the saccharines in the 2 tablespoons hot water. Add to the fruit.
7 Stir from time to time (to distribute the peel), then put in to jars and seal down.
NOTE: This should keep for some days.
To preserve for a longer period, pour into bottling jars, seal, giving screw band half turn back, stand in a pan of boiling water and sterilize for 5–10 minutes. Lift out, tighten screw band. Test for seal next day by seeing if the lid is tight.

Variations:

Lemon marmalade

As above, substituting lemons for oranges.

Sweet orange marmalade

As above but allow only 15 saccharine tablets and to 1 lb. sweet oranges add 1 lemon.

Drinks

Milk in your slimming diet

As stated in the introduction to this book, I have not tried to set out any formal diet. There are so many different types of diet to choose from nowadays, it would be very difficult to say that such-and-such a diet is ideal, or that one is necessarily better than another.
Most diets, however, do limit the amount of milk taken and it is generally ½ pint a day. Don't try and cut this out altogether, for milk is an essential food, but don't forget that the ½ pint will include the milk you use in coffee, tea and also for cooking.

Milk shakes

By whisking up the milk you can make it go further and provide a refreshing drink.
Put a very little finely crushed ice into a basin with the flavourings, as below, pour over the milk and whisk until fluffy, adding the saccharines or sugar substitute, if wished. With an electric mixer you can put it into the liquidiser goblet.

Flavourings for milk shakes

Banana: Add half a fairly ripe mashed banana to the milk, ice and saccharines.
Blackcurrant: Add a few fresh blackcurrants. Strain before using.
Coffee: Add strong coffee.
Lemon: Add the juice of a lemon.
Orange: Add the juice of an orange.
Raspberry: Add a few crushed raspberries.
Strawberry: Add a few crushed strawberries.

Having a drink on a diet

Alcohol is very high in calories, as you will see from the calorie chart on page 82. This does not mean that you should NEVER have a drink, but it does mean remembering that the drink must be counted in your day's diet. Also, it is obviously far more important to use the calories on good food.
Here are some ideas for fruit drinks, etc.

Citrus punch

no cooking

you will need:

4 oranges
3 lemons
1 grapefruit
1 quart soda water
6 saccharine tablets or sugar substitute
slices of fresh fruit, orange, apple, etc.

1 Squeeze the juice from the oranges, lemons and grapefruit.
2 Dissolve the saccharines or sugar substitute in a little hot water, and when it is cold add it to the fruit juices, together with the soda water and slices of orange and fresh fruit.

Fruit cup

no cooking

you will need:

3 sprigs of fresh mint	½ teaspoon powdered
1½ pints freshly made tea	ginger
juice of 3 oranges	2 tablespoons hot water
juice of 3 lemons	½ pint cold water
	ice cubes

1 Bruise the mint and pour the tea over the fruit juice.
2 Mix the ginger with the hot water, then add the cold water.
3 Mix all the ingredients, chill, and serve with ice cubes.

Lemonade

cooking time   5 minutes

you will need:

rind and juice of 4 lemons	6–12 saccharine tablets,
2 pints water	according to taste, or
	sugar substitute

1 Peel the rind thinly from the lemons and put this into a saucepan with the water.
2 Simmer gently for 5 minutes, then strain into a jug.
3 Add the crushed saccharine tablets or sugar substitute while hot then the juice of the lemons.
4 You may like to dilute slightly with soda water and ice.

Variations:

Orangeade

cooking time   5 minutes

As above, but use only 1½ pints of water to rind and juice of 4 medium sized oranges.

Fruitade

cooking time   5 minutes

As above, but use 1 grapefruit, 1 lemon and 1 orange. Peel the grapefruit rind very thinly.

Orange and ginger squash

no cooking   just a few minutes heating

you will need:

rind of 1 lemon	½ pint water
rind of 1 orange	juice of 2 oranges
1 oz. ginger	soda water
3–5 saccharine tablets	

1 Peel the lemon and orange thinly and put the peel, ginger and water into a pan.
2 Heat slowly and allow to infuse for 10 minutes.

3 Cool, and strain into the fruit juices.
4 Serve with soda water.

Soft fruit squash

cooking time   10–15 minutes

you will need:

8 oz. raspberries	1 quart cold water
8 oz. redcurrants	saccharine or sugar
4 oz. blackcurrants	substitute to taste

1 Put the prepared fruit with the water into a pan.
2 Simmer for 10–15 minutes and add sugar substitute.
3 Strain or sieve and serve cold.

Pineapple and orange cooler

no cooking

you will need:

1 pineapple	4–6 saccharine tablets
3 large oranges	or sugar substitute
1 quart boiling water	

1 Peel the pineapple, shred the flesh and mix it with the juice of the oranges.
2 Pour the boiling water on to this mixture, add saccharine tablets and set it aside to cool, stirring occasionally.
3 Strain.

Strawberry delight

no cooking

you will need:

1 lb. strawberries	2–3 saccharine tablets or
1 pint water	sugar substitute
	juice of 1 lemon

1 Mash the berries in a bowl and pour on the water.
2 Cover and allow to stand in a cool place for about 2 hours then strain the mixture through a sieve and the lemon juice and saccharines. Serve iced.

Iced tea cooler

cooking time   few minutes to make tea

you will need:

saccharine or sugar	½ lemon or orange
substitute	a few slices of lemon
1 pint hot tea	mint leaves
crushed ice	

1 Dissolve the saccharine in the hot tea, then pour the tea over crushed ice in a bowl. (Cooling the tea rapidly in this way makes it clear and sparkling.)
2 Add the juice of the lemon or orange.
3 Pour into tall glasses and serve with a slice of lemon and a mint leaf floating in each glass.

Iced tea

cooking time   few minutes to make tea

1 Make tea in the usual way, but allow a little more tea than normally. (China tea is usually preferred for this purpose.)
2 Pour into glasses or a jug containing crushed ice and add sliced lemon and saccharine or sugar substitute.
3 Chill and serve.

Iced coffee

Iced coffee is a delicious way of enjoying this beverage without adding too much milk.

1 Make the coffee in the usual way. Allow it to cool.
2 Pour over crushed ice and sweeten with saccharine or sugar substitute to taste.
3 A little cold milk can be added if wished.

Packed meals while on a diet

Many people who are overweight, and worried about it, nevertheless continue to eat a sandwich lunch every day. The reason is obvious. If you are going to take a packed meal to work, sandwiches and fruit are the easiest way of carrying food.

However, there are a number of ways of preparing an appetising packed meal without its containing an excess of starch. You will find several suggestions in the next few pages for good packed meals for people on a diet.

Carrying salads

Your salads can be carried quite easily and kept moist and fresh in either a screw top jar or in one of the modern plastic bags. They will make your packed meal much more interesting, and also help to keep down your calorie count.

Serve them with cheese, meat etc.

Carrying soups

A vacuum flask can be used to take hot soup, which will give you a good, filling start to your meal. You will find recipes on page 10.

Lettuce sandwiches

Choose large firm lettuce leaves and use these instead of slices of bread. Sandwich good thick slices of meat, cheese or flaked fish between the lettuce leaves and pack as you would for ordinary sandwiches.

Low-calorie open sandwiches

Whilst you are not completely avoiding bread when you make open sandwiches, you are at least using just half as much. Also if you use starch-reduced bread or crispbread the calories will again be reduced.

Put the meat, fish, whatever it may be, on top of the lightly buttered bread or crispbread. Then, instead of a second slice of bread, cover with a dry lettuce leaf or squares of greaseproof paper. In this way you can carry open sandwiches easily.

Sandwich spreads

The following sandwich spreads give you a most interesting filling that is not too fattening.

Cheese and horseradish spread

no cooking

you will need:

4 oz. cream cheese	4 oz. chopped
1 raw egg yolk	horseradish

Mix all the ingredients well together.

Cheese and tomato spread

no cooking

you will need:

2 halved tomatoes (with	salt
skins removed if wished)	pepper
5 oz. cream or soft cheese	dry mustard
herbs to taste	

1 Chop the tomatoes finely and blend with all the other ingredients.
2 A chopped hard-boiled egg could be added to this mixture.

Chicken spread

no cooking

you will need:

$\frac{1}{2}$ oz. soft chicken dripping	1 spring onion
parsley	chervil
chives	seasoning
6 oz. scraps of a cooked	
fowl	

Mix all ingredients together.

Egg and tomato spread

no cooking

you will need:

3 hard-boiled eggs   2 large skinned
seasoning   tomatoes

Chop and mix well together.

Liver spread

no cooking

you will need:

4–6 oz. cooked liver   1 spring onion
½ oz. melted butter or   seasoning
  chicken fat

Chop the spring onion very finely and blend
all ingredients together.

Roe pâté

no cooking

you will need:

8 oz. cooked cod's roe   1 oz. melted butter
  or herring roes   seasoning
dash of vinegar

Mix all ingredients together.

Ham pâté

no cooking

you will need:

4–6 oz. chopped ham   seasoning
1 oz. butter if ham is   2 tablespoons milk or
  very lean   salad dressing (page 44)

Cream together all the ingredients and add
a little chopped parsley if wished.

Lobster pâté

no cooking

you will need:

½ oz. melted butter   1 skinned tomato (if
seasoning   desired)
meat and fragments of   few drops of anchovy
  ½ lobster   essence

Mix all ingredients together.

Variations:

Substitute prawns, tuna fish, or shelled
shrimps for lobster.

Table of calorie values

Watching the calories: Unless one is a dietician
it is extremely difficult to know the calorie
value of various foods.
You may be following a diet which sets out
the number of calories you should have per
day. If it is very strict it could be as low as
1,000 but is more likely to be in the neighbour-
hood of 1,200–1,300 and the tables that follow
will give you a very good idea of how to keep
within that amount.

Food	Amount	Calories
Beverages		
Beer—ale, mild	½ pint	130
Beer—ale, pale	½ pint	150
Beer—ale, strong	½ pint	210
Beer—stout	½ pint	140
Cider	½ pint	120
Chocolate	1 cup	180
Cocoa (½ milk)	1 cup	110
Coffee—black	1 cup	0
Coffee—milk, no sugar	1 cup	30
Coffee—milk and sugar	1 cup	85
Fruit juice, diluted	1 glass	100
Malted drinks	1 cup	205
Mineral waters (artificial)	1 glass	100
Spirits (brandy, gin, rum, whisky)	1 oz.	75
Tea—milk, no sugar	1 cup	20
Tea—milk and sugar	1 cup	75
Wines—Port	2 oz.	90
Wines—Sherry	2 oz.	90
Wines, table—dry	4 oz.	70
Wines, table—sweet	4 oz.	90
Biscuits		
Biscuits—plain	1 oz.	105–115
Biscuits—sweet	1 oz.	135–145
Starch-reduced crispbread	1 oz.	110–120
Bread		
Bread—wholemeal, brown or white fresh or toasted	1 oz.	70
Starch-reduced roll	1 roll	18
Cakes		
Cake—plain	1 slice (2 oz.)	150

Food	Amount	Calories
Cake—rich, iced	1 slice (2 oz.)	210
Doughnut	2 oz.	195
Fruit cake	1 slice (2 oz.)	180

Cereals

Food	Amount	Calories
Arrowroot	1 oz.	100
Barley—pearl, dry	1 oz.	95
Cornflour—custard powder	1 oz.	100
Cornflakes and other breakfast cereals	1 oz.	106–110
Flour	1 oz.	100
Lentils—dried	1 oz.	164
Macaroni—uncooked	1 oz.	80–100
Maize meal—raw	1 oz.	95
Oatmeal	1 oz.	110
Rice—dry	1 oz.	90
Sago—dry	2 oz.	195
Soya flour (whole)	1 oz.	120
Soya flour, low fat	1 oz.	95
Spaghetti—dry	1 oz.	80
Tapioca—dry	2 oz.	195

Cheese

Food	Amount	Calories
Cheese—Cheddar	1 oz.	120
Cheese—cottage	1 oz.	40–50
Cheese—cream	1 oz.	145
Cheese—Dutch	1 oz.	90
Processed	1 oz.	120

Eggs

Food	Amount	Calories
Eggs—raw	1 (2 oz.)	80
Eggs—boiled	1	80
Eggs—poached	1	80–120 (if cooked in poacher with butter)
Eggs—fried	1	120–140 (depending on amount of fat)
Eggs—scrambled	1	ditto
Egg white	1	11
Egg yolk	1	69

Fats and milk

Food	Amount	Calories
Butter	$\frac{1}{4}$ oz.	65
Lard	$\frac{1}{4}$ oz.	60
Margarine	$\frac{1}{4}$ oz.	55
Milk—whole	$\frac{1}{2}$ pint	166–180
Milk–skimmed	$\frac{1}{2}$ pint	70
Milk—condensed	1 oz.	100
Milk—evaporated	1 oz.	45
Cream—light	1 oz.	55
Cream—heavy	1 oz.	100
Yoghourt	$\frac{1}{4}$ pint	100

Fish

Food	Amount	Calories
Crab	2 oz.	75
Cod Fillets	4 oz.	95
Haddock—fresh	4 oz.	115
Haddock—smoked	4 oz.	120
Halibut	4 oz.	140
Hake	4 oz.	90
Herring (1)	4 oz.	190
Lobster	4 oz.	65
Mackerel	4 oz.	90
Oysters	6 medium	65
Plaice	4 oz.	90
Salmon—fresh	4 oz.	155
Salmon—tinned	4 oz.	190
Salmon—smoked	2 oz.	175
Sardines	2 oz.	160
Shrimps	4 oz.	55
Sole	4 oz.	90
Sprats	4 oz.	170 if cooked without fat

Fruit

Food	Amount	Calories
Apple—cooked	5 oz.	75
Apple (1) approx.	4 oz.	45
Apricots—fresh ,,	4 oz.	30
Apricots—canned	4 oz.	60
Apricots—dried	1 oz.	50
Banana (1, average)		80–100
Blackberries—fresh	2 oz.	15
Blackberries—canned	4 oz.	15
Cherries—fresh	4 oz.	45
Cherries—canned	4 oz.	95
Coconut—fresh	1 oz.	170
Coconut—desiccated	1 oz.	180
Dates—dried	1 oz.	85
Figs—dried	2 oz.	115
Gooseberries	4 oz.	40
Grapefruit	4 oz.	25
Grapes	4 oz.	60
Lemon (1)	3 oz.	30
Loganberries	4 oz.	20
Melon	1 oz.	4
Olives	$\frac{1}{2}$ oz.	25
Orange (1)	6 oz.	40
Peaches—fresh	4 oz.	30
Peaches—canned	4 oz.	64
Pear—fresh	6 oz.	50
Pear—canned	2 halves	75
Pineapple—fresh	6 oz.	65
Pineapple—canned	6 oz.	120
Plums—fresh	4 oz.	30
Plums—canned	4 oz.	80
Prunes—dried	2 oz.	75
Raisins	2 oz.	125

Food	Amount	Calories
Raspberries—fresh	4 oz.	25
Rhubarb	4 oz.	5
Strawberries	4 oz.	30
Tangerines	2 small	40

Meats

Food	Amount	Calories
Bacon—lean	2 oz.	175
Bacon—fat	2 oz.	260
Beef—corned	4 oz.	280
Beef—roast lean	4 oz.	210 if fat up to 300
Ham—lean	4 oz.	265
Ham—fat	4 oz.	375
Heart	4 oz.	265
Kidneys	4 oz.	145
Lamb—lean	4 oz.	230
Lamb—fat	4 oz.	375
Liver	4 oz.	160
Mutton—lean	4 oz.	230
Mutton—fat	4 oz.	370
Pork—lean	4 oz.	270
Pork—fat	4 oz.	450
Sausages—beef	2 oz.	120
Sausages—pork	2 oz.	145
Steak	4 oz.	300
Tongue	4 oz.	290
Veal and Ham Pie	4 oz.	300
Veal—lean	4 oz.	145
Sweetbreads	4 oz.	250

Miscellaneous

Food	Amount	Calories
Cocoa powder	$\frac{1}{4}$ oz.	30
Gelatine	$\frac{1}{4}$ oz.	25
Honey	1 oz.	80
Ice cream (vanilla)	2 oz.	115
Jams and Jellies	$\frac{1}{2}$ oz.	35–60
Jelly—dessert	4 oz.	85–100
Junket	(as milk)	
Marmalade	$\frac{1}{2}$ oz.	35
Oils—salad	$\frac{1}{4}$ oz.	60
Pickles (non-thickened)	1 spoon	5–10
Soup—thin	4 oz.	20
Soup—creamy	5 oz.	80 upwards

Nuts

Food	Amount	Calories
Almond	1 oz.	170
Brazil nuts	1 oz.	90
Chestnuts	2 oz.	75
Peanuts	2 oz.	335
Walnuts	1 oz.	185

Poultry

Food	Amount	Calories
Chicken	4 oz.	165
Duck	4 oz.	190
Goose	4 oz.	355
Turkey	4 oz.	185

Sugar and sweets

Food	Amount	Calories
Sugar—white	$\frac{1}{2}$ oz.	55
Sugar—brown	$\frac{1}{2}$ oz.	50
Syrup	1 oz.	80
Boiled sweets	1 oz.	120 approx.
Chocolate—plain	1 oz.	150
Chocolate—milk	1 oz.	150

Vegetables

Food	Amount	Calories
Asparagus	6 stalks (3 oz.)	15
Beans—baked	4 oz.	100
Beans—broad	1 oz.	15
Beans—butter, boiled	1 oz.	25
Beans—haricot, dried	1 oz.	70
Beans—French or runner	4 oz.	15
Beetroot	2 oz.	15
Broccoli	4 oz.	15
Brussels sprouts	4 oz.	20
Cabbage	4 oz.	20
Carrots	2 oz.	15
Cauliflower	4 oz.	20
Celery	2 oz.	5
Cucumber	2 oz.	10
Endive	2 oz.	5
Leeks	4 oz.	15
Lettuce	2 oz.	10
Marrow	4 oz.	10
Mushrooms	2 oz.	2
Onions	4 oz.	25
Parsley	$\frac{1}{4}$ oz.	0
Parsnips	4 oz.	55
Peas—canned	4 oz.	25
Peas—fresh	4 oz.	75
Peas—dried	1 oz.	85
Pepper (vegetable)	1 oz.	10
Potatoes—boiled	2 medium (4 oz.)	95
Potatoes—fried	4 oz.	270
Radishes	1 oz.	2
Spinach	4 oz.	20
Tomatoes—fresh	4 oz.	20
Tomatoes—juice	4 oz.	25
Turnips	4 oz.	40

Index

O

Olives:
In Salads, 34
Beef with Olives, 27
Olive Dressing, 45
Olive-stuffed Tomatoes, 64

OMELETTES:
To Make, 50
Cheese Omelette, 50
Chicken Omelette, 50
Ham Omelette, 50
Mixed Vegetable Omelette, 50
Mushroom Omelette, 50
Omelette aux Fines Herbes, 50
Spinach Omelette, 50
Sweet Omelette Soufflé, 68
Tomato Omelette, 50

Onion:
In Salads, 34
Baked Onions, 61
Casseroled Onions, 61
Clear Onion Soup, 10
Creamed Eggs and Onion au Gratin, 49
Herrings with Onion Stuffing, 20
Onion Rings, 35
Onion Sauce, 44
Onion Savoury, 61
Onion Stuffed with Kidneys, 30
Pickled Onions, 46
Stuffed Onions, 61

Orange:
Cauliflower and Orange Salad, 37
Citrus Punch, 79
Fresh Orange Jelly, 69
Grape and Orange Cocktail, 8
Grapefruit and Orange Cocktail, 8
Lemon and Orange Jelly, 69
Orange Chiffon Cream, 71
Orange Cream Desserts, 71
Orange and Ginger Squash, 80
Orange Marmalade, 79
Orange Milk Jelly, 70–1
Orange Milk Shake, 79
Orange Mint Cocktail, 9
Orange Sauce, 75
Orange and Shrimp Salad, 41
Orange Sponge Pudding, 67
Orange Upside-down Pudding, 67
Pineapple and Orange Cooler, 80
Pineapple and Orange Juice Cocktail, 9
Three-Fruit Jelly, 69
Orangeade, 80

P

Packed Meals, 81
Paprika Pepper, 24
Parsley Butter, 78
Parsley Sauce, 44
PÂTÉ
Ham Pâté, 82
Lobster Pâté, 82
Roe Pâté, 82
Pear:
Pear Salad, 41
Peas, 5
Peppers, green and red:
Green Peppers with Cream Cheese, 62
Green or Red Pepper Salad, 39
Jamaican Peppers, 61
Red and Green Pepper Salad, 42
Stuffed Peppers, 62

PICKLES AND RELISHES:
Apple Chutney, 46
Pickled Cucumbers, 46
Pickled Onions or Shallots, 46
Pickled Red Cabbage, 46
Savoury Apples, 46
Pigeon:
Pigeons in Cider, 32
Pimento, 34
Pineapple:
Pineapple Berry Roundabout, 76
Pineapple and Cream Cheese Salad, 41
Pineapple and Grapefruit Baskets, 76
Pineapple and Melon Cocktail, 9
Pineapple and Orange Cooler, 80
Pineapple and Orange Juice Cocktail, 9
Piquant Chicken Grill, 31
Piquant Dressing, 45
Plaice:
Fillets of Plaice Délice, 18
Grilled Plaice with Grapes, 19
Plaice with Mushroom and Celery
    Stuffing, 20
Plaice with Prawns, 21
Plaice with Tomato Herb Stuffing, 21
Plaice and Tomato Pinwheels, 20
Plaice Whirls, 20
Plum:
Plum Fluff, 72
Plum Fool, 73
Poultry, *see* **Meat and Poultry**
Prairie Oyster, 51
Prawns:
As Cocktail Savouries, 13
American Prawn Salad, 35

Contents

KT-376-409

About inventions

An invention is a device or gadget that is designed and made for the first time. The person who makes the device is called an inventor. In this book, we look at inventions that help people to move about, who invented them and how they have changed over time.

Making life easier

Many types of transport have been invented because people want to improve their lives. For example, it is much easier to go by bus than to spend hours walking from place to place. Not only do inventions like buses make our lives easier by saving us time, but they have also changed the way we live.

EVERYDAY INVENTIONS

On the Move

Jane Bidder

W
FRANKLIN WATTS
LONDON • SYDNEY

This edition 2009

Franklin Watts
338 Euston Road
London NW1 3BH

Franklin Watts Australia
Hachette Children's Books
Level 17/207 Kent Street
Sydney NSW 2000

Series editor: Jennifer Schofield
Designer: Ross George
Picture researcher: Diana Morris
Artwork: Anthony Cutting

Acknowledgements:
The author would like to thank Mary Bellis
of http://inventors.about.com for her help
in researching this book.

AKG Images: 18b. Cody Images: 16t. Mary Evans
Picture Library; 6b, 9b, 10b, 12t, 12b, 13, 14, 16b,
19, 21, 22b, 24b. Chris Fairclough/Watts: 10t. Ford
Motor Company: 4b. National Museum of Roller
Skating, Lincoln, Nebraska, USA: 23. Parry/Topham:
25c. Photonews/Topham: 25b. Photri/Topham: 24.
Topham: 4t, 7b, 8t, 8b, 11, 15, 17, 18t, 20, 24t, 25.
James Witham/Team Suzuki: 3b, 14t.

Every attempt has been made to clear copyright.
Should there be any inadvertent omission please
apply to the publisher for rectification.

A CIP catalogue record for this book
is available from the British Library.

ISBN 978 0 7496 8948 3

Dewey Classification: 609

Printed in China

Franklin Watts is a division of Hachette Children's Books,
an Hachette UK company.
www.hachette.co.uk

Linked to each other

Many forms of transport have relied on one major breakthrough leading to changes elsewhere. For example, few inventions in this book would have happened without the invention of the wheel about 6,000 years ago.

Developing ideas

Not all inventions are thought of instantly - many of them are changed and improved over time. For example, the first motorbikes looked like bicycles with steam-powered engines. The engines were not very practical and soon they were replaced by petrol-powered engines. Today, not all motorbikes run on petrol - some run on electricity.

You will find timelines throughout this book. They show in date order when a specific breakthrough or invention occurred.

Sometimes the dates are very exact, but other times they point to a particular decade (period of ten years), for example the 1920s.

Use these timelines to keep track of when things happened.

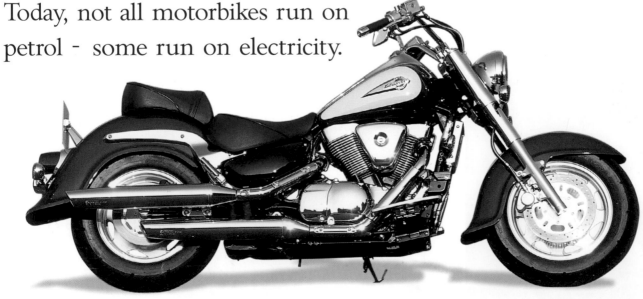

Cars

Today's cars have four wheels, and an engine that runs on petrol or diesel. They are made of metal and built for safety and comfort, with safety belts, airbags and padded seats. But cars were not always like this. The first car did not travel very fast and was built mainly from wood.

How does a car work?
A car's engine burns petrol or diesel and uses the energy this creates to turn the wheels.

The Fardier

The very first car was invented in 1769 and was called the Fardier. It had three wheels and was powered by steam. It could carry only two people and its top speed was just over 6 km/h.

Petrol power

The first car powered by petrol was probably built in 1889 by Gottlieb Daimler and Wilhelm Mayback. It was faster than the Fardier and could travel up to 16 km/h.

Fabulous Fords

A big breakthrough came in 1908 when Henry Ford's factory produced the Model T car. Over the next 19 years his company made more than 18 million cars. Ford still makes cars that are sold all over the world.

1769
Frenchman Nicholas-Joseph Cugnot makes the Fardier.

1889
The first petrol-driven car is built in Germany by Gottlieb Daimler and Wilhelm Mayback.

1908
The American Henry Ford produces the first Model T Ford.

1930s
Adolf Hitler asks Dr Ferdinand Porche to produce a cheap car for the German people. By 1938, the first Volkswagen Beetles are on the road.

1946
Rover makes the first gas turbine-powered motorcar.

1997
The Toyota Prius is sold in Japan. It is a hybrid car that runs on a mixture of petrol and electricity.

Bicycles

You may already know how to ride a bicycle or you may be learning how to turn the pedals. But did you know that the first bicycle had no pedals?

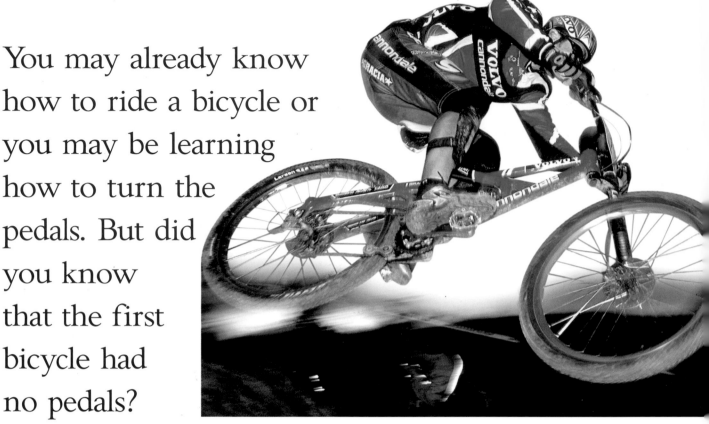

Foot power

The very first bicycle was known as the 'celeripede'. It had no pedals, gears or even a chain - you just sat on it and pushed it along with your feet.

Bone shakers

In 1861, Pierre Michaux fixed cranks, like pedals, onto the front wheels of the celeripede and called it a 'velocipede'. It was also known as a 'bone shaker', because your whole body shook when you rode it!

THE ROVER SAFETY BICYCLE (PATENTED).

Safer than any Tricycle, faster and easier than any Bicycle ever made. Fitted with handles to turn for convenience in storing or shipping. Far and away the best hill-climber in the market.

MANUFACTURED BY

STARLEY & SUTTON,

METEOR WORKS, WEST ORCHARD, COVENTRY, ENGLAND.

Price Lists of "Meteor," "Rover," "Despatch," and "Sociable" Bicycles and Tricycles, and the "Coventry Chair," Illustrated, free on application.

Rovers

The big break for bicycles came in 1895 when James Starley from England made the Rover. The Rover's pedals turned a gear wheel, which was linked to the back wheel by a chain. Like today's bicycles, the Rover's chain went around with the pedals, turning the wheels. The Rover was also known as the Safety Bicycle.

TIMELINE

1816
The celeripede is designed by the Frenchman J Niepce.

1861
France's Pierre Michaux makes the 'bone shaker'.

1870s
The Penny Farthing is invented — it has a large front wheel and a small back wheel.

1895
James Starley designs the Rover.

1930s
Bicycles now have rubber tyres and are easier to ride.

1940s
Tandem bicycles, with one bike joined to another, are invented.

1977
America's Joe Breeze builds a mountain bike, called Breezer No. 1. Only ten bikes are made, but the craze soon catches on.

Trains

In many countries around the world, trains are a fast and inexpensive way to travel. It is hard to imagine that the very first trains were carts pulled along rails by horses.

The Rocket

In 1829, George Stephenson from England built a new steam engine called the Rocket. It could pull a train for 56 km in less than two hours.

Railroads in the USA

Before trains ran across the USA, many western states were hard to reach. In the 1860s, two companies, the Central Pacific Railroad from California and the Union Pacific Railroad from New York, set out to build tracks across the USA. In 1869, a spike was put in the ground in Utah to mark where the two companies met.

Terrific TGVs

The TGV is France's high-speed train. TGVs and trains developed from the TGV run in countries around the world - for example in the USA, the Netherlands and South Korea. In 2003, a TGV travelling in England reached an amazing speed of 334.7 km/h.

TIMELINE

1804
England's Richard Trevithick builds the first steam engine.

1824
The first public railway opens in England, between Stockton and Darlington.

1829
George Stephenson makes the Rocket.

1830
The first public railroad is built in the USA, linking Baltimore and Ohio.

1920s
Electric and diesel trains begin to replace steam trains.

1964
A 'bullet' train is built in Japan; it can travel at more than 200 km/h.

1981
France's first TGV service runs from Paris to Lyon.

Buses

All over the world, buses cover great distances. In England's capital, London, each bus travels up to 1.2 million kilometres in its lifetime - that is the same as travelling to the Moon and back!

See the sights
The first sight-seeing buses were used in the USA in 1904. They could seat 15 people and travelled at up to 34 km/h.

Horse-power

Paris was the first city to use buses. The French buses were nothing like the buses of today - they were pulled by horses.

Paris Vécu. — Une Station d'Omnibus   L J & Cie. éd

Steam engines

In 1829, a steam-engined coach was designed in Britain. Although these coaches travelled faster than horse-drawn buses, not many were made because drivers had to pay a fee for using them on the roads.

Just like cars

In about 1919, when car engines were being developed, steam buses were replaced by petrol-run buses. A year later, in 1920, buses were also designed with covered tops and rubber tyres to make them more comfortable.

T I M E L I N E

1672
Buses are pulled by horses in Paris.

1829
England's George Shillibeer runs the first bus service in London.

1829
Sir Goldworthy Gurney of Britain makes the first steam-engined bus.

1904
Sight-seeing buses are used in the USA.

1914
Greyhound buses begin taking passengers from city to city in the USA.

1919
Petrol buses are used.

1920
Buses with covered roofs and rubber tyres are made.

Motorbikes

Some motorbikes can travel at incredible speeds of over 200 km/h, so it is hard to imagine that some of the early bikes travelled at speeds of only about 11km/h.

Howard-Roper's motorbike

In 1869, America's Sylvester Howard-Roper made a steam-engined motorbike. It was not very practical as its engine constantly needed topping up with coal.

The father of the motorbike

In 1885, the German engineer Gottlieb Daimler fitted a small petrol engine onto a wooden bicycle frame. He is sometimes called 'the father of the motorbike'.

steering lever

motor

seat

steady wheels

Harley Davidsons

The Harley Davidson Motor Company was founded in 1903 by William Harley and Arthur and Walter Davidson. They started racing their bikes in 1914 and became known as the 'Wrecking Crew' because they won so often.

TIMELINE

1869
The American Sylvester Howard-Roper designs the first steam motorbike.

1884
England's Edward Butler puts a petrol engine on a tricycle.

1885
Gottlieb Daimler fits a petrol engine on to a bicycle frame.

1894
Germany's Hildebrand and Wolfmueller make the first production motorbike.

1903
The Harley Davidson Motor Company is formed in the USA and develops its first motorbike.

2005
The American company eCycle begins testing a hybrid motorbike, that runs on electricity.

Aeroplanes

Inventors had been trying to make flying machines from as early as 400 BCE, when the Greek Archytas is said to have built a wooden pigeon that moved through the air with steam. Since then, flying machines have come a long way.

Girl power!
In 1930, Amy Johnson was the first woman to fly solo from England to Australia. It took her 19 days to make the 17,600-kilometre journey.

Flying around!

In 1903, the American brothers Wilbur and Orville Wright invented the first aeroplane. Their first flight lasted only 12 seconds.

Brilliant Boeings

In 1969, the first Boeing 747 (see left) was built. At the time, the 747 was the largest passenger aeroplane - its tail alone was taller than a six-storey building! The first 747 could carry 400 people and could fly at more than 1,000 km/h. Many of today's planes are updated versions of the 747.

Concorde

Concorde was the world's first passenger aeroplane to travel faster than the speed of sound. These supersonic planes were used for passengers from 1976. However, in 2003 they were taken out of service.

TIMELINE

1903
The Wright brothers fly the first aeroplane.

1909
The Frenchman Louis Bleriot flies across the English Channel in his Bleriot XI monoplane.

1930
Amy Johnson flies from England to Australia.

1937
Germany's Hans von Ohain builds the first jet engine, the He178.

1960
The Hawker P1127 is able to make vertical take-offs and landings.

1969
The Boeing 747 is built.

1976
Concorde carries passengers for the first time.

2005
A new plane, the A380, is flown. It can carry more than 550 people.

Wheelchairs

We know a type of wheelchair was used as long ago as 530 BCE. Since then, wheelchairs have come a long way - from those that fold up to the lightweight three-wheeled models that athletes use.

Farfler's wheel chair

In 1655 Stephen Farfler, a paraplegic (someone who is not able to use his legs), designed his own wheelchair. It enabled him to move himself about using his arms, rather than relying on someone to push him.

Paralympics
The first Olympic-style games for disabled athletes were held in 1960. Today, the Paralympic Games include basketball, athletics and tennis for wheelchair athletes.

Bath chairs

In 1783, John Dawson from Bath in England developed the Bath chair. It looked like a large reclining chair with two big wheels at the back and one or two small wheels at the front.

Folding chairs

In 1933, the American Herbert A Everest wanted a wheelchair that he could get in and out of a car. He asked the English engineer HC Jennings to make a folding wheelchair. The wheelchair was a great success and modern folding wheelchairs are based on this design.

530 BCE
The first type of wheelchair is shown on a Greek vase.

1595
A special 'invalid's chair' is built for Spain's King Philip II.

1655
Stephen Farfler designs his own wheelchair.

1783
The Bath chair is made in England.

1912
The first electric wheelchair is made.

1933
A folding wheelchair is made by England's HC Jennings.

1948
The first sporting event for wheelchair users is held in England.

Motorscooters

Sometimes one invention leads to another. For example, scooters were developed after motorbikes were made so that people had a cheaper way to get around.

The Autoped

It is unclear who invented the first motorscooter. However, some reports claim that the first one was called the Autoped. It had no seat, so the rider had to stand and move the steering column. Early scooters could travel at 16 km/h.

Parascooting!
During the Second World War, armies used parachutes to drop scooters near their troops so that they could move about.

The wasp

Soon after the Second World War, the Piaggio aeroplane factory developed a new scooter. When its owner, Enrico Piaggio heard the scooter, he exclaimed, 'Sembra una vespa' ('It's like a wasp') and the name Vespa stuck.

Lambretta scooters

The first Lambretta was made in 1947 to fill the need for cheap transport in Italy. It had a second seat (see above), making it able to carry passengers.

TIMELINE

1915
The Autoped is made in America.

1919
England's Granville Bradshaw makes the ABC Scootmota.

1920
Motorscooters become fashionable for men and women.

1940s
Scooters are used by armies during the Second World War.

1946
The first Vespas are made in Italy.

1947
Ferdinando Innocenti's company makes the first Lambretta.

Roller skates

Just as scooters followed on from the invention of the motorbike, so roller skates were developed from ice skates.

Roll away

The first roller skate was invented by Belgium's Jean-Joseph Merlin in 1760. Merlin would skate and play the violin at the same time, as a party trick. However, Merlin had not found a way to stop suddenly, and one day he collided with a large mirror, injuring himself.

Get your skates on!

During the 1860s, James L Plimpton designed a roller skate with two pairs

of wheels on the heel and toe. He also opened his own skating rink.

Later, in the 1880s, the Americans Richardson and Raymond improved on skates' wheels by adding ball bearings, which made the skates go faster and more smoothly.

Ball bearings
Ball bearings are tiny steel balls that fit between a wheel and an axle. They keep the wheel moving smoothly.

Much lighter

During the 1940s, roller skates were designed with plastic wheels instead of metal, to make them lighter on the feet. They also had toe-stops for braking.

TIMELINE

1760
Merlin designs a boot for roller skating.

1860s
James Plimpton from America makes a better roller skate and opens a rink.

1880s
Richardson and Raymond make skates with ball bearings.

1940s
Roller skates are made from plastic to make them lighter and easier to skate in.

1989
America's Scott and Brennan Olson start a company to make a new kind of roller skate, called roller blades.

1990s
Skates are made from titanium to make them even lighter.

Helicopters

Helicopters are amazing flying machines. Their blades turn really fast to make them move, and because they do not need runways like aeroplanes do, they can take off and land in small spaces.

First flight

The first helicopter is said to have been invented in 1907 by a Frenchman called Paul Cornu. However, it flew for only a few seconds. As with many inventions, it took many other people to work on helicopters before they really took off!

Sikorsky's success

One of the most successful helicopter designers was Russia's Igor Sikorsky. He started designing helicopters in 1910. After many designers tried to build helicopters, Sikorsky finally designed the VS-300 in 1940. The VS-300 was used as a model for other helicopters and, as a result, Sikorsky is known as the 'father' of helicopters.

Helicopter power!
In 1986, a Westland Lynx is said to have flown at the amazing speed of 402 km/h.

Westland Lynx

In 1971, the Westland Lynx helicopter flew for the first time. Today, countries such as Denmark, Britain and France still use the Westland Lynx as a military helicopter.

TIMELINE

1907
France's Paul Cornu invents the first helicopter.

1910
Igor Sikorsky starts designing helicopters.

1924
France's Etienne Oehmichen flies a helicopter for 1 kilometre.

1940
The VS-300 is designed by Igor Sikorsky.

1971
The first Westland Lynx is made.

More inventions

Every day, people use many other forms of transport, too. For example, children are pushed in baby buggies or pushchairs to get them from place to place and many people use boats or ferries to travel to work or to go on holiday.

Baby buggies

It is difficult for young children to get about - especially if they are too small to walk. The first baby buggy was designed by England's William Kent in 1733. However, the big breakthrough in baby buggies came in 1965 when Owen Maclaren made the first folding buggy.

Ferries

Boats have been used to to ferry people across water for thousands of years. The first steam-powered ferry crossing of the English Channel is thought to have been in 1820. Today, ferries are used all over the world, transporting peope, cars and even trucks.

Pushscooters

Children's scooters have been around for about 100 years. In the early 2000s, folding metal scooters were made and they became popular with both children and adults.

Many inventions that help us to travel from place to place have wheels. Although the wheel has been around since prehistoric times, the rubber tyre used on many of the forms of transport is quite a new invention.

In 1888, John Boyd Dunlop had the idea of trapping air inside a rubber tyre after watching his son riding a bicycle with solid rubber tyres.

Then in 1895, the first air-filled car tyre was invented by the Michelin brothers. They showed off their new tyres on a car called Eclair.

Since the Michelin brothers' tyres, tyre manufacturers have developed tyres for different vehicles, such as trucks, tractors and aeroplanes.

Timeline

530 BCE

Wheelchairs are used – they look like beds on wheels.

1655

Stephen Farfler designs his own wheelchair.

1672

The first bus is invented.

1760

Jean-Joseph Merlin designs a boot for roller skating.

1769

The first steam-powered car is made by Nicholas Cugnot.

1804

Richard Trevithick invents the first steam train.

1816

The first bicycle is invented.

1860s

James Plimpton adds more wheels to roller skates.

1869

The first motorbike is made by Sylvester Howard-Roper.

1889

A petrol-driven car is built by Daimler and Mayback.

1903

The first aeroplane is made by the Wright brothers.

1907

Paul Cornu invents the first helicopter.

1908

Henry Ford makes a Model T car.

1915

The Autoped motorscooter is made.

1920

Buses with covered roofs and rubber tyres are made.

1933

A folding wheelchair is made.

1938

The first Volkswagen Beetles are on the road.

1946

The first Vespas are made in Italy.

1964

A 'bullet' train is built in Japan.

1968

The Boeing 747 is built.

1976

Concorde carries passengers for the first time.

1981

France's first TGV service runs from Paris to Lyon.

1997

The Toyota Prius, a hybrid car, is sold in Japan.

2005

The A380 aeroplane is flown for the first time.

Glossary

Axle
The pin or rod found in the centre of the wheel. The wheel turns around the axle.

Coal
A natural, brown or black hard substance that is burnt as a fuel.

Hitler, Adolf (1889–1945)
The German ruler during the Second World War.

Hybrid
A car or motorbike that is developed from other cars and motorbikes.

Invalid
Someone who has a long term illness or disability.

Paraplegic
Someone who cannot move the lower part of his or her body and often needs to use a wheelchair.

Prehistoric
From a time long before history was recorded.

Public
For everyone's use.

Railroad
A track laid with rails so that the wheels of a train can run on it.

Steady wheels
Smaller wheels that are attached to the back wheels of bicycles and motorbikes to keep the bike upright and steady.

Steering column
The pole found on a bicycle, car or motorbike that the steering wheel is attached to. The steering wheel is used to change direction.

Solo
Alone.

Supersonic
Faster than the speed of sound.

Titanium
A shiny white metal that is found in rocks. It is lightweight, strong and does not rust easily.

Websites

www.nationalgeographic.com/features/96/inventions/
Have loads of fun playing games about inventions.

www.howstuffworks.com
Find out how everyday inventions work by searching for them on this website.

www.cybersteering.com/trimain/history/ecars.html
Follow the development and history of the car, from its early days to today's speed machines.

www.pedalinghistory.com
Find out everything there is to know about bicycles from who invented them to how they work.

www.bbc.co.uk/schools/famouspeople
Click on George Stephenson to learn all about the steam engine and how he developed it.

http://kids.discovery.com/convergence/wright/wright.html
Follow America's Wright brothers, Wilbur and Orville, as they build their first aeroplane and take off!

www.sciencemuseum.org.uk/online/flights/index.asp
Go on a virtual tour of the British Science Museum and follow the development of famous inventions.

www.rollerskatingmuseum.com
Tour a roller-skating museum.

Note to parents:

Every effort has been made by the publishers to ensure that the websites in this book are suitable for children, that they are of the highest educational value, and that they contain no inappropriate or offensive material. However, due to the nature of the Internet, it is impossible to guarantee that the contents of these sites will not be altered. We strongly advise that Internet access is supervised by a responsible adult.

Index